THE CITY & GUILDS TEXTBOOK
LEVEL 1 DIPLOMA IN
BRICKLAYING

THE CITY & GUILDS TEXTBOOK

LEVEL 1 DIPLOMA IN
BRICKLAYING

COLIN FEARN

MIKE JONES

CLAYTON RUDMAN

SERIES TECHNICAL EDITOR
MARTIN BURDFIELD

About City & Guilds

City & Guilds is the UK's leading provider of vocational qualifications, offering over 500 awards across a wide range of industries, and progressing from entry level to the highest levels of professional achievement. With over 8500 centres in 100 countries, City & Guilds is recognised by employers worldwide for providing qualifications that offer proof of the skills they need to get the job done.

Equal opportunities

City & Guilds fully supports the principle of equal opportunities and we are committed to satisfying this principle in all our activities and published material. A copy of our equal opportunities policy statement is available on the City & Guilds website.

Copyright

First edition 2013

ISBN 9780851932668

Publisher Fiona McGlade
Development Editor James Hobbs
Production Editor Lauren Heaney

Cover design by Design Deluxe
Illustrations by Barking Dog Art and Palimpsest Book Production Ltd
Typeset by Palimpsest Book Production Ltd, Falkirk, Stirlingshire
Printed in the UK by Cambrian Printers Ltd

British Library Cataloguing in Publication Data

A catalogue record for this book is available from the British Library.

Publications

For information about or to order City & Guilds support materials, contact 0844 534 0000 or centresupport@cityandguilds.com. You can find more information about the materials we have available at www.cityandguilds.com/publications.

Every effort has been made to ensure that the information contained in this publication is true and correct at the time of going to press. However, City & Guilds' products and services are subject to continuous development and improvement and the right is reserved to change products and services from time to time. City & Guilds cannot accept liability for loss or damage arising from the use of information in this publication.

City & Guilds
1 Giltspur Street
London EC1A 9DD

T 0844 543 0033

www.cityandguilds.com

publishingfeedback@cityandguilds.com

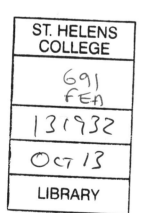

CONTENTS

FOREWORD

Whether in good times or in a difficult job market, I think one of the most important things is for young people to learn a skill. There will always be a demand for talented and skilled individuals who have knowledge and experience. That's why I'm such an avid supporter of vocational training. Vocational courses provide a unique opportunity for young people to learn from people in the industry, who know their trade inside out.

Careers rarely turn out as you plan them. You never know what opportunity is going to come your way. However, my personal experience has shown that if you haven't rigorously learned skills and gained knowledge, you are unlikely to be best placed to capitalise on opportunities that do come your way.

When I left school, I went straight to work in a butcher shop, which was a fantastic experience. It may not be the industry I ended up making my career in, but being in the butchers shop, working my way up to management level and learning from the people around me was something that taught me a lot about business and about the working environment.

Later, once I trained in the construction industry and was embarking on my career as a builder, these commercial principles were vital in my success and helped me to go on to set up my own business. The skills I had learned gave me an advantage and I was therefore able to make the most of my opportunities.

Later still, I could never have imagined that my career would take another turn into television. Of course, I recognise that I have had lucky breaks in my career, but when people say you make your own luck, I think there is definitely more than a grain of truth in that. People often ask me what my most life-changing moment has been, expecting me to say winning the first series of Big Brother. However, I always answer that my most life changing moment was deciding to make the effort to learn the construction skills that I still use every day. That's why I was passionate about helping to set up a construction academy in the North West, helping other people to acquire skills and experience that will stay with them for their whole lives.

After all, an appearance on a reality TV show might have given me a degree of celebrity, but it is the skills that I learned as a builder that have kept me in demand as a presenter of DIY and building shows, and I have always continued to run my construction business. The truth is, you can never predict the way your life will turn out, but if you have learned a skill from experts in the field, you'll always be able to take advantage of the opportunities that come your way.

Craig Phillips
City & Guilds qualified bricklayer, owner of a successful construction business and television presenter of numerous construction and DIY shows

ABOUT THE AUTHORS

COLIN FEARN

CHAPTERS 1 AND 2

I was born, grew up and continue to live in Cornwall with my wife, three children and Staffordshire bull terrier.

As a qualified carpenter and joiner, I have worked for many years on sites and in several joinery shops.

I won the National Wood Award for joinery work and am also a Fellow of the Institute of Carpenters, holder of the Master Craft certificate and have a BA in Education and Training.

I was until recently a full-time lecturer at Cornwall College, teaching both full-time students and apprentices.

I now work full-time as a writer for construction qualifications, practical assessments, questions and teaching materials for UK and Caribbean qualifications.

In my spare time I enjoy walks, small antiques and 'keeping my hand in' with various building projects.

CLAYTON RUDMAN

CHAPTERS 3 AND 5

The construction industry is large and varied. Personally the choice of trade to specialise in was easy. I knew from an early age that bricklaying was my future.

Working on site and studying to achieve my Level 2 and 3 qualifications was difficult, but with the right resources and tutors it was enjoyable.

I came into teaching straight from the building site as a young man having been inspired by my tutors to pass on the experience, knowledge and skills I gained by building my own homes to others.

30 years on I still enjoy teaching.

My career progressed and over time I have taught at every level, working my way up to Head of School in one of Wales's largest further education colleges.

I am still teaching and at present combine it with a quality role within a very successful school of construction.

MIKE JONES

CHAPTERS 4 AND 6

I currently work as a Construction Lecturer and Section Leader in the Brickwork Section at Cardiff and Vale College in South Wales.

I have worked in education for the past 10 years and my previous construction industry career spanned over 30 years of work, ranging from skilled trade activities to supervisory and site management positions.

My aim in teaching practice is to impart to learners the great job satisfaction that can be gained from becoming a skilled practitioner in bricklaying. I enjoy taking the time to encourage the development of lasting talents and rewarding skills.

MARTIN BURDFIELD

SERIES TECHNICAL EDITOR

I come from a long line of builders and strongly believe that you will find a career in the construction industry a very rewarding one. Be proud of the work you produce, it will be there for others to admire for many years.

As an apprentice I enjoyed acquiring new knowledge and learning new skills. I achieved the C&G Silver Medal for the highest marks in the Advanced Craft Certificate and won the UK's first Gold Medal in Joinery at the World Skills Competition. My career took me on from foreman, to estimator and then works manager with a number of large joinery companies, where I had the privilege of working on some prestigious projects.

Concurrent with this I began working in education. I have now worked in further education for over 35 years enjoying watching learners' skills improve during their training. For 10 years I ran the Skillbuild Joinery competitions and was the UK Training Manager and Chief Expert Elect at the World Skills Competition, training the UK's second Gold Medallist in Joinery.

Working with City & Guilds in various roles over the past 25 years has been very rewarding.

I believe that if you work and study hard that anything is possible.

HOW TO USE THIS TEXTBOOK

Welcome to your City & Guilds Level 1 Diploma in Bricklaying textbook. It is designed to guide you through your Level 1 qualification and be a useful reference for you throughout your career. Each chapter covers a unit from the 6705 Level 1 qualification, and covers everything you will need to understand in order to complete your written or online tests and prepare for your practical assessments.

Please note that not all of the chapters will cover the learning outcomes in order. They have been put into a logical sequence as used within the industry and to cover all skills and techniques required.

Throughout this textbook you will see the following features:

Blade

The 'working' part of the trowel that allows manipulation of the mortar

Useful words – **Words in bold in the text are explained in the margin to help your understanding.**

INDUSTRY TIP

Keep a tape measure in your pocket or on your belt and put your spirit level down in the same place each time after you use it. This speeds things up when you want to check your work.

Industry tips – Useful hints and tips related to working in the construction industry.

ACTIVITY

Calculate how many bricks and blocks you will need to build a cavity wall 6290mm long and 1350mm high.

Activities – These are suggested activities for you to complete.

STEP 1 Apply a small amount of mortar to the header face of the brick.

Step by steps – These steps illustrate techniques and procedures that you will need to learn in order to carry out bricklaying tasks.

Look at the blockwork used in the foundations of 'Our House'. What methods have been used to put it together?

Case Study: Kayleigh

Kayleigh is to build a small single garage at the rear of a house. It must be big enough to accommodate an estate car and give enough room to allow the user to get out and walk around the car. The garage has two windows, an up-and-over door at the front and a flat roof. She has been asked to provide a plan of this garage for the client.

Draw this garage to a scale that will fit onto an A4 piece of paper. Include the window openings, the door, the thickness of the walls (which will be single block) and the piers.

Mortar	
	A mixture of soft sand and cement mixed with water and other additives if required, eg plasticiser, colouring or lime. It is used for laying bricks.

At the end of every chapter are some 'Test your knowledge' questions. These questions are designed to test your understanding of what you have learnt in that chapter. This can help with identifying further training or revision needed. You will find the answers at the end of the book.

INTRODUCTION

This book has been written to support students studying bricklaying at Level 1. By studying this book, you should receive a thorough grounding in the skills and knowledge you will need to complete your course and either progress to Level 2, or enter the workforce. You will learn about the wider construction industry and how it works, as well as the skills and techniques you will need in order to work as a bricklayer. You will be able to work safely on site using the correct tools and equipment to lay bricks and blocks in order to produce masonry structures.

In addition to the features listed on the previous page, which are there to help you retain the information you will need to become a bricklayer, this textbook includes a large trade dictionary. Use this for reference in class and in the workshop. Become familiar with the terms and techniques, and pay attention to the skills you need to master. If you put in the effort, you will be rewarded with a satisfying and successful career in construction.

ACKNOWLEDGEMENTS

I would like to thank my dear wife Helen for her support in writing for this book. My thanks go to the other chaps (Clay, Martin and Mike) for all their help! I dedicate my work to Matt, Tasha and Daisy, and not forgetting Floyd and Mrs Dusty.

Colin Fearn

I dedicate this book to my tutor, employer, and friend Mr L E Marks from whom I developed my experience in the construction industry. Thanks also to my wife for all her support and hard work during our 28 years of building houses.

Clayton Rudman

Firstly, my thanks to John Ennis for starting my journey in education. Many thanks to my fellow authors and the staff at City & Guilds for their support and encouragement. I've also appreciated the input and suggestions of my colleagues Paul Sebburn, Craig Jones and Pete Bradwick at CAVC. Finally, thanks to my long-suffering wife Sue and the rest of my family, who supported me (and proofread my material) throughout.

Mike Jones

To my gorgeous wife Clare, without whose constant support, understanding and patience I would not have been able to continue. To Matthew and Eleanor, for not being there on too many occasions, normal service will be resumed. Finally, my parents, to whom I will always be grateful.

Martin Burdfield

City & Guilds would like to sincerely thank the following:

For invaluable bricklaying expertise
Paul Brown, Steve Everton, Glen Smith and Julian Walden.

For their help with photoshoots
Andrew Buckle (photographer), Paul Reed, Akeem Callum, Frankie Slattery, Wahidur Rahman and all of the staff at Hackney Community College.

For supplying pictures for the book cover
Andrew Buckle.

TRADE DICTIONARY

Industry term	Definition and regional variations
Aggregates	The coarse mineral material, such as sharp sand and graded, crushed stone (gravel), used in making mortar and concrete.
Air brick	A perforated building block to allow ventilation through walls.
Alignment	To place something in line.
Approved Code of Practice (ACoP)	ACoP gives practical advice for those involved in the construction industry in relation to using machinery safely. ACoP has a special legal status and employers and employees are expected to work within its guidelines.
Architect	A trained professional who designs a structure and represents the client who wants the structure built. They are responsible for the production of the working drawings. They supervise the construction of buildings or other large structures.

Industry term	Definition and regional variations
Architectural technician 	A draftsperson who works in an architectural practice. They usually prepare the location drawings for a building.
Arris 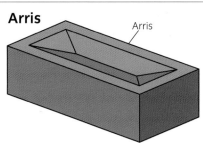	Any straight sharp edge of a brick formed by the junction of two faces.
Asbestos 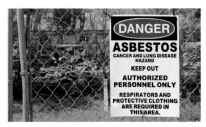	A naturally occurring mineral that was commonly used for a variety of purposes including: insulation, fire protection, roofing and guttering. It is extremely hazardous and can cause a serious lung disease known as asbestosis.
Banding 	Whole sections of brickwork that differ in colour and stand out from the main body of work.
Bed 	Mortar upon which the brick is laid or bedded.
Bed joint 	Continuous, horizontal mortar joint supporting the bricks.

Industry term	Definition and regional variations
Bill of quantities BILL OF QUANTITIES (Assuming Civil Engineering Standard Method of M Number Item description CLASS A: GENERAL ITEMS Specified Requirements	Produced by the quantity surveyor and describes everything that is required for the job based on the drawings, specification and schedules. It is sent out to contractors and ensures that all the contractors are pricing for the job using the same information.
Blade	The 'working' part of the trowel that allows manipulation of the mortar.
Blended	When bricks have gone through a process that disperses variations in colour and size of bricks to avoid unwanted patterns emerging.
Bolster	A broad bladed chisel used for cutting bricks and blocks.
Bond/Bonding	The arrangement or pattern of laying bricks and blocks to spread the load through the wall, also for strength and appearance.
Boundary	A line marking the end of an area.
Brick trowel	Used for spreading and rolling mortar. *Regional variation: walling trowel*
British Standards Institute (BSI)	The authority that develops and publishes standards in the UK.

Industry term	Definition and regional variations
Broken bond 	The use of part bricks to make good a bonding pattern where full bricks will not fit in.
Builder's square 	A tool for checking corners. A builder's square that is set at an angle of 90° will form a right-angled quoin.
Building line 	The front line of the building. Note that this can be on or behind the frontage line. (*See also* Line.)
Building Regulations	A series of documents that set out legal requirements for the standards of building work.
CAD drawings 	Drawings which are created using computer-aided design.
Calibrate	To ensure no air is trapped in a water level.
Cavity batten 	A timber batten slightly narrower than the cavity dimension with cords or wires attached. It rests in the cavity on the wall ties to catch mortar droppings and can be withdrawn as the work progresses using the cords or wires.
Cavity wall 	Walls built in two separate skins/leaves (usually of different materials) with a void held together by wall ties.

Industry term	Definition and regional variations
Chimney stack 	The portion of the chimney containing the tops of the flues which passes through and projects above the roof.
Cladded 	When a surface has been covered in another material, eg plastic or timber.
Class A block 	A high quality fair-faced block.
Common bricks 	Bricks of medium quality used for ordinary walling work where no special face finish is required. Bricks are manufactured to dimensions and tolerances decided by official institutes. In the UK, this is the British Standards Institute.
Concrete 	Material made up of cement, sand and stone of varying size and in varying proportions. It is mixed with water.
Core holes 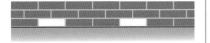	Temporary holes left in a cavity wall at ground level to enable mortar droppings to be removed from cavity.

Industry term	Definition and regional variations
Corner blocks 	Plastic or wooden blocks used to hold the line to a stopped end.
Corner profiles 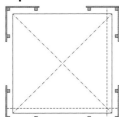	A type of profile used for marking the position of corners, which can be up to three metres high. Most bricklayers find corner profiles easier to use as they have level lines which can be used to form building lines in two directions. (*See also* Profiles.)
Course 	A horizontal row of blocks or bricks laid on a mortar bed.
Cross-section 	A view that shows an imaginary slice through a structure to reveal interior details.
Damp proof course (DPC) 	A layer or strip of watertight material placed in a joint of a wall to prevent the passage of water. Fixed at a minimum of 150mm above finished ground level.
Damp proof membrane (DPM) 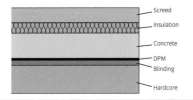	A layer or sheet of watertight material, incorporated into a solid floor to prevent the rise of moisture.

Industry term	Definition and regional variations
Datum point	A fixed point or height from which to take reference levels. They may be permanent Ordnance Bench Marks (OBMs) or Temporary Bench Marks (TBMs). The datum point is used to transfer levels across a building site. It represents the finished floor level (FFL) on a dwelling.
Dead load	The self weight of all the materials used to construct the building.
Dense	Material that is hard and heavy for its volume ie dense blocks.
Detector	Used to locate the services when working on the foundations of the structure. This equipment works by sending out an electronic pulse. to tell how deep the metal of the services is.
Double handling	Moving materials twice or even three times before use. This wastes time and energy when bricklaying.
Dry bond	A method of spacing bricks or blocks without mortar to sort out potential problems with the bond.
Dry silo mixer	A major piece of equipment that contains all the dry materials to produce mortar mixed on demand. It minimises waste because it only produces mortar as it is needed.
Durability	How capable a product is of withstanding wear and tear or decay.

Industry term	Definition and regional variations
Efflorescence 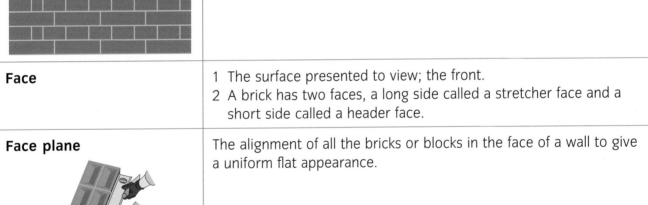	A white deposit which may form on the surface of new bricks if the latter contain a high proportion of mineral salts.
Elevation	Any face of a building or wall on a plan.
Engineering bricks	Hard dense bricks of regular size used for carrying heavy loads, eg in bridge buildings, heavy foundations.
English bond	A type of one-brick bond. This bond is set out with alternating courses of headers and stretchers. It is the strongest bonding arrangement possible.
Face	1 The surface presented to view; the front. 2 A brick has two faces, a long side called a stretcher face and a short side called a header face.
Face plane	The alignment of all the bricks or blocks in the face of a wall to give a uniform flat appearance.
Fair face	Indicating face work of neat appearance. Flemish bond is often referred to as fair-faced.

Industry term	Definition and regional variations
Finished floor level (FFL)	This is the height of the finished floor level in a property. Represented with a datum point, and horizontal DPC is often installed at this height.
Flashing 	Flashings are commonly made from lead and are used to provide waterproofing at joints where roofing materials meet walls and around chimneys. May also be made from zinc or copper.
Flemish bond 	A type of one-brick bond that consists of alternating headers and stretchers within a course. The headers in a course are centred above the stretchers in the course below to give a strong Quarter bond and also to produce an interesting pattern.
Floors 	The structured layers of a building, eg ground floor, first floor, second floor.
Flush joint 	Bed and perp joint finished with a trowel flush to the material used.
Footings	The substructure below ground level. These are projecting courses at the base of a wall.
Forklift 	The main piece of machinery used for moving heavy materials, such as bricks. The driver of the forklift is trained to work in a safe manner.

Industry term	Definition and regional variations
Foundation	Used to spread the load of a building to the sub-soil.
Fracture	A crack or break in a hard object or material.
Friction	Resistance between two surfaces, for example the surface of the concrete foundation and the soil around it.
Frog	The indentation in a brick.
Frontage line	The front edge of the building plot, usually taken from the centre line of a road or kerb edge, from which the building line is established.
Full joint	The joint has no gaps or voids that will allow water penetration. *Regional variation: flush joint*
Gauge	The dimensions of a bed joint (10mm) and a brick depth (65mm) added together (75mm). This needs to be kept uniform and accurate so that the final height of the wall is kept to specification. This is known as keeping to gauge and requires frequent checking with a tape measure or gauge rod.

Industry term	Definition and regional variations
Gauge rod 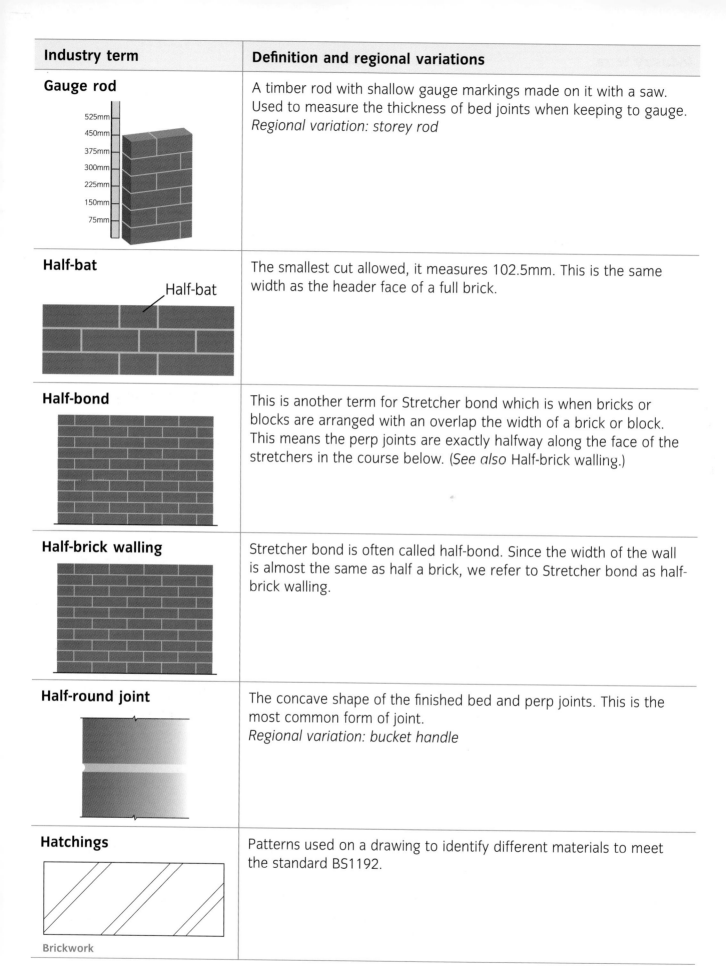	A timber rod with shallow gauge markings made on it with a saw. Used to measure the thickness of bed joints when keeping to gauge. *Regional variation: storey rod*
Half-bat	The smallest cut allowed, it measures 102.5mm. This is the same width as the header face of a full brick.
Half-bond	This is another term for Stretcher bond which is when bricks or blocks are arranged with an overlap the width of a brick or block. This means the perp joints are exactly halfway along the face of the stretchers in the course below. (*See also* Half-brick walling.)
Half-brick walling	Stretcher bond is often called half-bond. Since the width of the wall is almost the same as half a brick, we refer to Stretcher bond as half-brick walling.
Half-round joint	The concave shape of the finished bed and perp joints. This is the most common form of joint. *Regional variation: bucket handle*
Hatchings Brickwork	Patterns used on a drawing to identify different materials to meet the standard BS1192.

Industry term	Definition and regional variations
Header face	The end face of a brick, which is its shortest side. It is 102.5mm wide.
Hypotenuse	The longest side of a right-angled triangle. It is always opposite the right angle.
Imposed load	Additional loads that may be placed on the structure, eg people, furniture, wind and snow.
Improvement notice	Issued by an HSE or local authority inspector to formally notify a company that improvements are needed to the way it is working.
Indent	A recess formed in the brickwork or blockwork to accommodate future work.
Industrial Standards	Minimum standards of quality of completed work universally adopted within the industry.
Insulation	Materials used to retain heat and improve the thermal value of the building. Can also be used in managing sound transfer.
Interpret	To understand the meaning of information, eg information from working drawings and specifications.
Jointer	A tool used to provide a finish to the joints. It produces a concave finish to the mortar just before it begins to harden, to create a half-round joint.

Industry term	Definition and regional variations
Jointing 	To make a finish to the mortar faces as work proceeds, eg half-round jointing.
Junctions 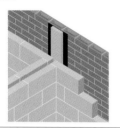	Methods of joining together walls set at angles.
Kinetic lifting 	A method of lifting that ensures the risk of injury is reduced.
Leaves 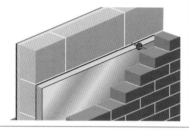	The two walls that make up a cavity wall to comply with current building regulations. They are tied together with wall ties. *Regional variation: skin*
Levelling 	To make sure that two points are at the same height.
Lime 	A fine powdered material traditionally used in mortars.

Industry term	Definition and regional variations
Line and pins 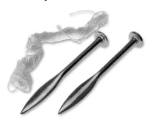	A string used to guide the blocks or bricks to make them straight.
Line 	The straightness of the block or brickwork.
Lintel 	A horizontal member for spanning an opening, such as a door, to support the structure above, usually made from steel or concrete.
Manufacturer's instructions 	Guidelines given by the manufacturer on conditions of use.
Method statement 	A description of the intended method of carrying out a task, often linked to a risk assessment.
Mortar 	A mixture of soft sand and cement mixed with water and other additives if required, eg plasticiser, colouring or lime. It is used for laying bricks.

Industry term	Definition and regional variations
Optical level 	A levelling operation using eyesight. The level is accurate up to 30m with a variation of +/-5mm. Bricklayers use optical levels when the length of construction exceeds the straight edge. The level is placed on a tripod and used with a staff or rod to transfer lines between two or more points.
Ordnance bench mark (OBM) 	They are a given height on an Ordnance Survey map. This fixed height is described as a value, eg so many metres above sea level (as calculated from the average sea height at Newlyn, Cornwall).
Pallets 	A storage base used to carry and store materials such as bricks or blocks.
Perimeter 	The distance around an object or room.
Perp joints 	Small vertical joints which join two bricks together. They are at right angles to the bed.
Personal protective equipment (PPE)	This is defined in the Regulations as 'all equipment (including clothing affording protection against the weather) which is intended to be worn or held by a person at work and which protects against one or more risks to a person's health or safety.' For example, safety helmets, gloves, eye protection, high-visibility clothing, safety foot-wear and safety harnesses.

Industry term	Definition and regional variations
Piers	Brickwork used for support in walls or as pillars, attached and detached.
Plasticiser	An additive that is used to make the mortar pliable and easier to work with. This is safer and easier to use than the traditionally used hydrated lime in powder form.
Plumb	The verticality of brickwork. Plumbing should be started from the second course, using a spirit level.
Pointing	The process of applying a finish to the joints in brickwork using mortar.
Profiles	Boards fixed horizontally to ground pegs at the ends of a wall before construction commences in order that lines may be stretched across to mark the position of the foundations and wall.
Programme of work	A series of events where the order of activities and the amount of time involved has been planned out. This is usually shown in the form of a bar or gantt chart. *Regional variation: work schedule*
Prohibition notice	Issued by an HSE or local authority inspector when there is an immediate risk of personal injury. Receiving one means you are breaking health and safety regulations.

Industry term	Definition and regional variations
Property 	A building and the land belonging to it.
Pulled line 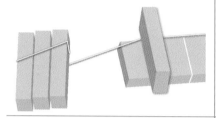	A tight line fixed to bricks or blocks.
Quarter bond 	Bonds in a wall that has a width equal to the length of the stretcher face of a brick (and are therefore referred to as 'one-brick' walling). The bonding arrangement shows bricks lapping each other by a quarter of a length (as in English and Flemish bond). Used where a thicker wall is needed for greater strength.
Queen Closer 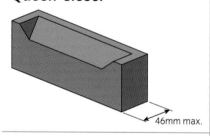	A brick split along its length to produce a cut of 46mm. It is cut to the size of half a header face, and is used next to quoin bricks to establish the start of a bonding arrangement. Also used in indents for junction walls.
Quoins 	The vertical external angles (corners) in walling. Builder's squares are used to check that the corner is square, before you lay any blocks or bricks.
Racking back 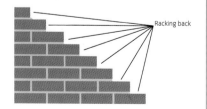	The process of building up the corners or the ends of a wall to produce a plumb reference point that guides accurate laying of the rest of the wall in between. *Regional variation: raking back*

Industry term	Definition and regional variations
Ranging line 	A line stretched between profiles to mark the position of a wall end or foundation. The line is made from nylon and is waterproof. *Regional variation: builder's line*
Reclaim	To re-use resources, eg to use crushed bricks for hardcore.
Regular-shaped	To give a square, or rectangular shape to a building or masonry structure.
Render	When a brick, stone or block face is covered in a layer of sand and cement.
Return	The proportion of brickwork at right angles to the face of the wall.
Reverse bond	In the same course, starting with a stretcher and ending with a header.
Risk assessment	An assessment of the hazards and risks associated with an activity and the reduction and monitoring of them.
Rule of thumb	Industry recognised practice, eg when calculating the number of blocks required for a wall the rule of thumb is 10 blocks per 1m².
Scale	The ratio of the size on a drawing to the size of the real thing that it represents. It is impossible to fit a full-sized drawing of a building onto a sheet of paper, so it is necessary to scale the size of the building to enable it to fit. Scale rules are used to drawn scaled down buildings on paper.

Industry term	Definition and regional variations
Scutch hammer 	A bricklayer's hammer with interchangeable finishing heads for trimming and tidying bricks and blocks. *Regional variation: comb hammer*
Section view 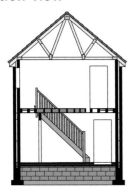	Drawings that show a cut away view of a structure.
Segregated waste 	Separated into groups or categories, eg glass, metal and wood. Waste is often segregated to support recycling and contribute to sustainability.
Services 	Those provided by the utility companies, eg gas, electricity and water.
Setting out 	A method of locating the position of building works ready for starting work. This involves marking and positioning where a structure will be built. Accuracy is very important when setting out as mistakes here can prove costly.
Solid walls 	Walls of a thickness of one brick and greater. Unlike cavity walls, there are usually only two materials to consider; either bricks and mortar or blocks and mortar.

Industry term	Definition and regional variations
Specification 	A contract document that gives information about the quality of materials and standards of workmanship required.
Spirit level 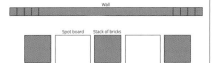	A measuring tool to make sure the work is level and plumb. Spirit levels come in a range of sizes; the size most commonly used by bricklayers is 1.2m, but sometimes 2m spirit levels are used to help with the construction of blockwork.
Spot board 	A board made of durable material roughly 600mm x 600mm, on which mortar is placed. The boards are raised up from ground level by supporting it on blocks.
Stopped end 	The vertical end of a wall.
Straight edge	An accurately proportioned implement with parallel edges made of timber or aluminium and up to 3m in length.
Straps 	Plastic binding holding bricks or blocks together on a pallet. Straps are dangerous and can cut hands or legs.
Stretcher bond 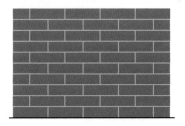	The bricks or blocks are arranged with an overlap the width of a brick or block. This means the perp joints are exactly halfway along the face of the stretchers in the course below.

Industry term	Definition and regional variations
Stretcher face Stretcher face 	The long face of a brick when laid. It measures 215mm wide.
Substructure	All brick and blockwork below DPC.
Superstructure	All brick and blockwork undertaken above DPC.
Sustainability 	To continue to do something with minimal long-term effects on the environment. Building materials can be sustainable if they are chosen carefully.
Tape measure 	A measuring tool used to set out and check dimensions. A range of tape measures in various sizes is required when setting out a structure. Tape measures vary in range from 3m to 30m.
Tarpaulin 	Sheet material, usually plastic, used to protect materials.
Temporary bench mark (TBM) 	Unlike an OBM, this is only temoprary and is set up on site. These can be timber pegs surrounded by concrete.

Industry term	Definition and regional variations
Temporary profiles	Using a dense cut block to weigh down the line to stop the pulled line from moving.
Thermoplastic materials	Plastics which become soft when heated and hard when cooled. Some DPCs contain thermoplastic materials.
Tolerances	Allowable variations between the specified measurement and the actual measurement.
Tooled/Ironed	Using steel tools to create a specified type of joint.
Top soil	The top 150mm of soil containing vegetable matter.
Trowel	Used to lay bricks. It has a 'blade', which allows you to manipulate the mortar when laying.
Volatile organic compound (VOC)	The volatile organic compounds measure shows how much pollution a product will emit into the air when in use.

Industry term	Definition and regional variations
Weather-struck joint	An angled joint, which means one side of the joint is pressed further into the joint than the other.
Weighted	Use of dense cut block to weigh down the line to stop the pulled line from moving.
Well graded sand	Sand that has large, medium and small grains, such as 'pit sand' or 'sea-dredged sand'. Used in mortar.

Chapter 1
Unit 201: Health, safety and welfare in construction

A career in the building industry can be a very rewarding one, both personally and financially. However, building sites and workshops are potentially very dangerous places; there are many potential hazards in the construction industry. Many construction operatives (workers) are injured each year, some fatally. Regulations have been brought in over the years to reduce accidents and improve working conditions.

By reading this chapter you will know about:

1 The health and safety regulations, roles and responsibilities.

2 Accident and emergency reporting procedures and documentation.

3 Identifying hazards in the workplace.

4 Health and welfare in the workplace.

5 Handling materials and equipment safely.

6 Access equipment and working at heights.

7 Working with electrical equipment in the workplace.

8 Using personal protective equipment (PPE).

9 The cause of fire and fire emergency procedures.

HEALTH AND SAFETY LEGISLATION

According to the Health and Safety Executive (HSE) figures, in 2011/12:

- Forty-nine construction operatives were fatally injured. Twenty-three of these operatives were self-employed. This compares with an average of 59 fatalities over the previous five years, of which an average of 19 fatally injured construction operatives were self-employed.

- The rate of fatal injury per 100,000 construction operatives was 2.3, compared with a five-year average of 2.5.

- Construction industry operatives were involved in 28% of fatal injuries across all industry sectors and it accounts for the greatest number of fatal injuries in any industry sector.

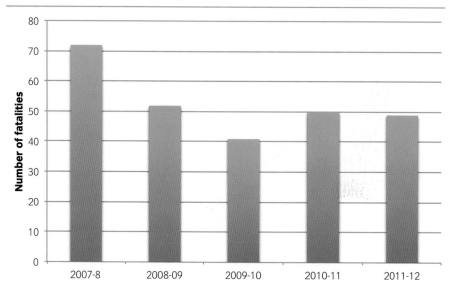

Number and rate of fatal injuries to workers in construction (RIDDOR)

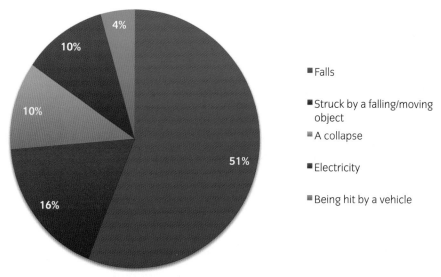

Proportion of fatalities in 2011/12 in construction

Health and safety legislation and great efforts made by the industry have made workplaces much safer in recent years. It is the responsibility of everyone involved in the building industry to continue to make it safer. Statistics are not just meaningless numbers – they represent injuries to real people. Many people believe that an accident will never happen to them, but it can. Accidents can:

- have a devastating effect on lives and families

- cost a lot financially in injury claims

- result in prosecution

- lead to job loss if an employee broke their company's safety policy.

Employers have an additional duty to ensure operatives have access to welfare facilities, eg drinking water, first aid and toilets, which will be discussed later in this chapter.

If everyone who works in the building industry pays close attention to health, safety and welfare, all operatives – including you – have every chance of enjoying a long, injury-free career.

UK HEALTH AND SAFETY REGULATIONS, ROLES AND RESPONSIBILITIES

In the UK there are many laws (legislation) that have been put into place to make sure that those working on construction sites, and members of the public, are kept healthy and safe. If these laws and regulations are not obeyed then prosecutions can take place. Worse still, there is a greater risk of injury and damage to your health and the health of those around you.

Standard construction safety equipment

The principle legislation which relates to health, safety and welfare in construction is:

- Health and Safety at Work Act (HASAWA) 1974

- Control of Substances Hazardous to Health (COSHH) Regulations 2002

- Reporting of Injuries, Diseases and Dangerous Occurrences Regulations (RIDDOR) 1995

- Construction, Design and Management (CDM) Regulations 2007

- Provision and Use of Work Equipment Regulations (PUWER) 1997

- Manual Handling Operations Regulations 1992

- Personal Protective Equipment (PPE) at Work Regulations 1992

- Work at Height Regulations 2005
- Lifting Operations and Lifting Equipment Regulations (LOLER) 1998
- Control of Noise at Work Regulations 2005
- Control of Vibration at Work Regulations 2005.

HEALTH AND SAFETY AT WORK ACT (HASAWA) 1974

The Health and Safety at Work Act (HASAWA) 1974 applies to all workplaces. Everyone who works on a building site or in a workshop is covered by this legislation. This includes employed and self-employed operatives, subcontractors, the employer and those delivering goods to the site. It not only protects those working, it also ensures the safety of anyone else who might be nearby.

KEY EMPLOYER RESPONSIBILITIES

The key employer health and safety responsibilities under HASAWA are to:

- provide a safe working environment
- provide safe access (entrance) and egress (exit) to the work area
- provide adequate staff training
- have a written health and safety policy in place
- provide health and safety information and display the appropriate signs
- carry out risk assessments
- provide safe machinery and equipment and to ensure it is well-maintained and in a safe condition
- provide adequate supervision to ensure safe practices are carried out
- involve trade union safety representatives, where appointed, in matters relating to health and safety
- provide personal protective equipment (**PPE**) free of charge, ensure the appropriate PPE is used whenever needed, and that operatives are properly supervised
- ensure materials and substances are transported, used and stored safely.

PPE

This is defined in the Personal Protective Equipment at Work Regulations 1992 as 'all equipment (including clothing affording protection against the weather) which is intended to be worn or held by a person at work and which protects against one or more risks to a person's health or safety.'

Risk assessments and method statements

The HASAWA requires that employers must carry out regular **risk assessments** to make sure that there are minimal dangers to their employees in a workplace.

Risk assessment

An assessment of the hazards and risks associated with an activity and the reduction and monitoring of them

---

Risk Assessment

Activity / Workplace assessed: Return to work after accident
Persons consulted / involved in risk assessment
Date:
Reviewed on:

Location:
Risk assessment reference number:
Review date:
Review by:

Significant hazard	People at risk and what is the risk Describe the harm that is likely to result from the hazard (e.g. cut, broken leg, chemical burn etc.) and who could be harmed (e.g. employees, contractors, visitors etc.)	Existing control measure What is currently in place to control the risk?	Risk rating Use matrix identified in guidance note Likelihood (L) Severity (S) Multiply (L) * (S) to produce risk rating (RR)				Further action required What is required to bring the risk down to an acceptable level? Use hierarchy of control described in guidence note when considering the controls needed	Actioned to: Who will complete the action?	Due date: When will the action be complete by?	Completion date: Initial and date once the action has been completed
			L	S	RR	L/M/H				
Uneven floors	Operatives	Verbal warning and supervision	2	1	2	m	None applicable	Site supervisor	Active now	Ongoing
Steps	Operatives	Verbal warning	2	1	2	m	None applicable	Site supervisor	Active now	Ongoing
Staircases	Operatives	Verbal warning	2	2	4	m	None applicable	Site supervisor	Active now	Ongoing

	Likelihood			
		1 Unlikely	2 Possible	3 Very likely
Severity	1 Slight/minor injuries/minor damage	1	2	3
	2 Medium injuries/significant damage	2	4	6
	3 Major injury/extensive damage	3	6	9

Likelihood
3 – Very likely
2 – possible
1 – Unlikely

Severity
3 – major injury/extensive damage
2 – medium injury/significant damage
1 – Slight/minor damage

1 – Low risk, action should be taken to reduce the risk if reasonably practicable
2, 3, 4 – Medium risk, is a significant risk and would require an appropriate level of resource
6 & 9 – High risk , may require considerable resource to mitigate. Control should focus on elimination of risk, if not possible control should be obtained by following the hierarchy of control

123 type risk assessment

A risk assessment is a legally-required tool used by employers to:

- identify work hazards

- assess the risk of harm arising from these hazards

- adequately control the risk.

Risk assessments are carried out as follows:

1 Identify the hazards. Consider the environment in which the job will be done. Which tools and materials will be used?

2 Identify who might be at risk. Think about operatives, visitors and members of the public.

3 Evaluate the risk. How severe is the potential injury? How likely is it to happen? A severe injury may be possible but may also be very improbable. On the other hand a minor injury might be very likely.

4 If there is an unacceptable risk, can the job be changed? Could different tools or materials be used instead?

5 If the risk is acceptable, what measures can be taken to reduce the risk? This could be training, special equipment and using PPE.

6 Keep good records. Explain the findings of the risk assessment to the operatives involved. Update the risk assessment as required – there may be new machinery, materials or staff. Even adverse weather can bring additional risks.

A **method statement** is required by law and is a useful way of recording the hazards involved in a specific task. It is used to communicate the risk and precautions required to all those involved in the work. It should be clear, uncomplicated and easy to understand as it is for the benefit of those carrying out the work (and their immediate supervisors).

Inductions and tool box talks

Any new visitors to and operatives on a site will be given an induction. This will explain:

- the layout of the site

- any hazards of which they need to be aware

- the location of welfare facilities

- the assembly areas in case of emergency

- site rules.

Tool box talks are short talks given at regular intervals. They give timely safety reminders and outline any new hazards that may have arisen because construction sites change as they develop. Weather conditions such as extreme heat, wind or rain may create new hazards.

KEY EMPLOYEE RESPONSIBILITIES

The HASAWA covers the responsibilities of employees and subcontractors:

- You must work in a safe manner and take care at all times.

- You must make sure you do not put yourself or others at risk by your actions or inactions.

Method statement

A description of the intended method of carrying out a task, often linked to a risk assessment

INDUSTRY TIP

The Construction Skills Certification Scheme (CSCS) was set up in the mid-90s with the aim of improving site operatives' competence to reduce accidents and drive up on-site efficiency. Card holders must take a health and safety test. The colour of card depends on level of qualification held and job role. For more information see www.cscs.uk.com

ACTIVITY

Think back to your induction. Write down what was discussed. Did you understand everything? Do you need any further information? If you have not had an induction, write a list of the things you think you need to know.

INDUSTRY TIP

Remember, if you are unsure about any health and safety issue always seek help and advice.

- You must co-operate with your employer in regard to health and safety. If you do not you risk injury (to yourself or others), prosecution, a fine and loss of employment. Do not take part in practical jokes and horseplay.

- You must use any equipment and safeguards provided by your employer. For example, you must wear, look after and report any damage to the PPE that your employer provides.

- You must not interfere or tamper with any safety equipment.

- You must not misuse or interfere with anything that is provided for employees' safety.

FIRST AID AND FIRST-AID KITS

First aid should only be applied by someone trained in first aid. Even a minor injury could become infected and therefore should be cleaned and a dressing applied. If any cut or injury shows signs of infection, becomes inflamed or painful seek medical attention. An employer's first-aid needs should be assessed to indicate if a first-aider (someone trained in first aid) is necessary. The minimum requirement is to appoint a person to take charge of first-aid arrangements. The role of this appointed person includes looking after the first-aid equipment and facilities and calling the emergency services when required.

First-aid kits vary according to the size of the workforce. First-aid boxes should not contain tablets or medicines.

INDUSTRY TIP

The key employee health and safety responsibilities are to:
- work safely
- work in partnership with your employer
- report hazards and accidents as per company policy.

INDUSTRY TIP

Employees must not be charged for anything given to them or done for them by the employer in relation to safety.

INDUSTRY TIP

In the event of an accident, first aid will be carried out by a qualified first aider. First aid is designed to stabilise a patient for later treatment if required. The casualty may be taken to hospital or an ambulance may be called. In the event of an emergency you should raise the alarm.

ACTIVITY

Your place of work or training will have an appointed first-aider who deals with first aid. Find out who they are and how to make contact with them.

ACTIVITY

Find the first-aid kit in your workplace or place of training. What is inside it? Is there anything missing?

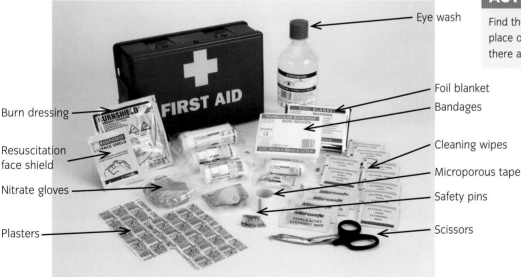

Eye wash
Foil blanket
Bandages
Cleaning wipes
Microporous tape
Safety pins
Scissors
Burn dressing
Resuscitation face shield
Nitrate gloves
Plasters

First-aid kit

SOURCES OF HEALTH AND SAFETY INFORMATION

Source	How they can help
Health and Safety Executive (HSE)	A government body which oversees health and safety in the workplace. It produces health and safety literature such as the **Approved Code of Practice** (ACoP).
Construction Skills	The construction industry training body produces literature and is directly involved with construction training.
The Royal Society for the Prevention of Accidents (ROSPA)	It produces literature and gives advice.
The Royal Society for Public Health	An independent, multi-disciplinary charity which is dedicated to the promotion and protection of collective human health and wellbeing.
Institution of Occupational Safety and Health (IOSH)	A chartered body for health and safety practitioners. The world's largest health and safety professional membership organisation.
The British Safety Council	It helps businesses with their health, safety and environmental management.

HEALTH AND SAFETY EXECUTIVE (HSE)

The HSE is a body set up by the government. The HSE ensures that the law is carried out correctly and has extensive powers to ensure that it can do its job. It can make spot checks in the workplace, bring the police, examine anything on the premises and take things away to be examined.

If the HSE finds a health and safety problem that breaks health and safety law it might issue an **improvement notice** giving the employer a set amount of time to correct the problem. For serious health and safety risks where there is a risk of immediate major injury, it can issue a **prohibition notice** which will stop all work on site until the health and safety issues are rectified. It may take an employer, employee, self-employed person (subcontractor) or anyone else

Approved Code of Practice

ACoP gives practical advice for those in the construction industry in relation to using machinery

INDUSTRY TIP

There are many other trade organisations, eg the Timber Research and Development Association (TRADA) which also offer advice on safe practices.

ACTIVITY

You have been asked to give a tool box talk because of several minor injuries involving tripping on site. What topics would you include in this talk?

INDUSTRY TIP

To find out more information on the sources in the table, enter their names into a search engine on the internet.

Improvement notice

Issued by an HSE or local authority inspector to formally notify a company that improvements are needed to the way it is working

Prohibition notice

Issued by an HSE or local authority inspector when there is an immediate risk of personal injury. They are not issued lightly and if you are on the receiving end of one, you are clearly breaking a health and safety regulation involved with the building process to court for breaking health and safety legislation.

The HSE provides a lot of advice on safety and publishes numerous booklets and information sheets. One example of this is the Approved Code of Practice (ACoP) which applies to wood working machinery. The ACoP has a special legal status and employers and employees are expected to work within its guidelines.

The duties of the HSE are to:

■ give advice

■ issue improvement and prohibition notices

■ caution

■ prosecute

■ investigate.

The Approved Code of Practice booklet is available free online

CONTROL OF SUBSTANCES HAZARDOUS TO HEALTH (COSHH) REGULATIONS 2002

The Control of Substances Hazardous to Health (COSHH) Regulations 2002 controls the use of dangerous substances, eg preservatives, fuel, solvents, adhesives, cement and oil-based paint. These have to be moved, stored and used safely without polluting the environment. It also covers hazardous substances produced while working, eg wood dust produced when sanding or drilling.

Hazardous substances may be discovered during the building process, eg lead-based paint or asbestos. These are covered by separate regulations.

When considering substances and materials that may be hazardous to health an employer should do the following to comply with COSHH:

■ Read and check the COSHH safety data sheet that comes with the product. It will outline any hazards associated with the product and the safety measures to be taken.

■ Check with the supplier if there are any known risks to health.

■ Use the trade press to find out if there is any information about this substance or material.

■ Use the HSE website, or other websites, to check any known issues with the substance or material.

When assessing the risk of a potentially dangerous substance or material it is important to consider how operatives could be exposed to it. For example:

Example of COSHH data sheet

- by breathing in gas or mist

- by swallowing it,

- by getting into their eyes

- through their skin, either by contact or through cuts.

Safety data sheets

Products you use may be 'dangerous for supply'. If so, they will have a label that has one or more hazard symbols. Some examples are given here.

These products include common substances in everyday use such as paint, bleach, solvent or fillers. When a product is 'dangerous for supply', by law, the supplier must provide you with a safety data sheet. Note: medicines, pesticides and cosmetic products have different legislation and don't have a safety data sheet. Ask the supplier how the product can be used safely.

Safety data sheets can be hard to understand, with little information on measures for control. However, to find out about health risks and emergency situations, concentrate on:

- Sections 2 and 16 of the sheet, which tell you what the dangers are;
- Sections 4-8, which tell you about emergencies, storage and handling.

Since 2009, new international symbols have been gradually replacing the European symbols. Some of them are similar to the European symbols, but there is no single word describing the hazard. Read the hazard statement on the packaging and the safety data sheet from the supplier.

European symbols

 Toxic Very toxic Harmful Irritant

 Highly flammable Extremely flammable Explosive   Dangerous to the environment

Oxidising   Corrosive

New International symbols

Hazard checklist

☐ Does any product you use have a danger label?
☐ Does your process produce gas, fume, dust, mist or vapour?
☐ Is the substance harmful to breathe in?
☐ Can the substance harm your skin?
☐ Is it likely that harm could arise because of the way you use or produce it?
☐ What are you going to do about it?
   - Use something else?
   - Use it in another, safer way?
   - Control it to stop harm being caused?

CONTROL MEASURES

The control measures below are in order of importance.

1 Eliminate the use of the harmful substance and use a safer one. For instance, swap high **VOC** oil-based paint for a lower VOC water-based paint.

2 Use a safer form of the product. Is the product available ready-mixed? Is there a lower strength option that will still do the job?

VOC

The volatile organic compounds measure shows how much pollution a product will emit into the air when in use

INDUSTRY TIP

Product data sheets are free and have to be produced by the supplier of the product.

3 Change the work method to emit less of the substance. For instance, applying paint with a brush releases fewer VOCs into the air than spraying paint. Wet grinding produces less dust than dry grinding.

4 Enclose the work area so that the substance does not escape. This can mean setting up a tented area or closing doors.

5 Use extraction or filtration (eg a dust bag) in the work area.

6 Keep operatives in the area to a minimum.

7 Employers must provide appropriate PPE.

Paint with high VOC content

ACTIVITY

Think of three substances in your workplace or place of training that might be hazardous to health. Can you find a COSHH data sheet for each? (They can often be found on the internet if you search for the product.)

European symbols

Toxic   Very toxic   Harmful   Irritant

Highly   Extremely   Explosive   Dangerous
flammable   flammable   to the
                                              environment

Oxidising   Corrosive

New International symbols

Toxic   May explode   Irritant
             when heated

Causes fire   Explosive   Dangerous to the
                                environment

Intensifies fire   Long term   Corrosive
                 health hazard

COSHH symbols. The international symbols will replace the European symbols in 2015.

INDUSTRY TIP

For more detailed information on RIDDOR visit the HSE webpage at www.hse.gov.uk/riddor.

REPORTING OF INJURIES, DISEASES AND DANGEROUS OCCURRENCES REGULATIONS (RIDDOR) 1995

Despite all the efforts put into health and safety, incidents still happen. The Reporting of Injuries, Diseases and Dangerous Occurrences Regulations (RIDDOR) 1995 state that employers must report to the HSE all accidents that result in an employee needing more than seven days off work. Diseases and dangerous occurrences must also be reported. A serious occurrence which has not caused an injury (a near miss) should still be reported because next time it happens things might not work out as well.

Below are some examples of injuries, diseases and dangerous occurrences which would need to be reported:

- A joiner cuts off a finger while using a circular saw.

- A plumber takes a week off after a splinter in her hand becomes infected.

- A ground operative contracts **leptospirosis**.

- A labourer contracts dermatitis (a serious skin problem) after contact with an irritant substance.

- A scaffold suffers a collapse following severe weather, unauthorised alteration or overloading but no-one is injured.

Leptospirosis

Also known as Weil's disease, this is a serious disease spread by rats and cattle

The purpose of RIDDOR is to enable the HSE to investigate serious incidents and collate statistical data. This information is used to help reduce the number of similar accidents happening in future and to make the workplace safer.

INDUSTRY TIP

Accidents do not just affect the person who has the accident. Work colleagues or members of the public might be affected and so will the employer. The consequences may include:

- a poor company image (this may put potential customers off)
- loss of production
- insurance costs increasing
- closure of the site
- having to pay sick pay
- other additional costs.

New HSE guidelines require employers to pay an hourly rate for time taken by the HSE to investigate an accident. This is potentially very costly.

An F2508 injury report form

Although minor accidents and injuries are not reported to HSE, records must be kept. Accidents must be recorded in the accident book. This provides a record of what happened and is useful for future reference. Trends may become apparent and the employer may take action to try and prevent that particular type of accident occurring again.

ACTIVITY

You have identified a potential risk. What action should you take? Make notes.

CONSTRUCTION, DESIGN AND MANAGEMENT (CDM) REGULATIONS 2007

The Construction, Design and Management (CDM) Regulations 2007 focus attention on the effective planning and management of construction projects, from the design concept through to maintenance and repair. The aim is for health and safety considerations to be integrated into a project's development, rather than be an inconvenient afterthought. The CDM Regulations reduce the risk of harm to those that have to work on or use the structure throughout its life, from construction through to **demolition**.

The CDM regulations play a role in safety during demolition

Demolition

When something, often a building, is completely torn down and destroyed

CDM Regulations protect workers from the construction to demolition of large and complex structures

The CDM Regulations apply to all projects except for those arranged by private clients, ie work that isn't in furtherance of a business interest. Property developers need to follow the CDM Regulations.

Under the CDM Regulations, the HSE must be notified where the construction work will take:

- more than 30 working days or

- 500 working days in total, ie if 100 people work for 5 days (500 working days) the HSE will have to be notified.

DUTY HOLDERS

Under the CDM Regulations there are several duty holders, each with a specific role.

Duty holder	Role
Client	This is the person or organisation who wishes to have the work done. The client will check that: ■ all the team members are competent ■ the management is suitable ■ sufficient time is allowed for all stages of the project ■ welfare facilities are in place before construction starts. HSE notifiable projects require that the client appoints a CDM co-ordinator and principal contractor, and provides access to a health and safety file.
CDM co-ordinator	Appointed by the client, the co-ordinator advises and assists the client with CDM duties. The co-ordinator notifies the HSE before work starts. This role involves the co-ordination of the health and safety aspects of the design of the building and ensures good communication between the client, designers and contractors.
Designer	At the design stages the designer removes hazards and reduces risks. The designer provides information about the risks that cannot be eliminated. Notifiable projects require that the designer checks that the client is aware of their CDM duties and that a CDM co-ordinator has been appointed. The designer will also supply information for the health and safety file.
Principal contractor	The principal contractor will plan, manage and monitor the construction in liaison with any other involved contractors. This involves developing a written plan and site rules before the construction begins. The principle contractor ensures that the site is made secure and suitable welfare facilities are provided from the start and maintained throughout construction. The principal contractor will also make sure that all operatives have site inductions and any further training that might be required to make sure the workforce is competent.
Contractor	Subcontractors and self-employed operatives will plan, manage and monitor their own work and employees, co-operating with any main contractor in relation to site rules. Contractors will make sure that all operatives have any further training that might be required to make sure they are competent. A contractor also reports any incidents under RIDDOR to the principal contractor.
Operatives	Operatives need to check their own competence: Can you carry out the task you have been asked to do safely? Have you been trained to do this type of activity? Do you have the correct equipment to carry out this activity? You must follow all the site health and safety rules and procedures and fully co-operate with the rest of the team to ensure the health and safety of other operatives and others who may be affected by the work. Any health and safety issues must be reported.

A client, a contractor and an operative looking over building plans ahead of construction

WELFARE FACILITIES REQUIRED ON SITE UNDER THE CDM REGULATIONS

The table below shows the welfare facilities that must be available on site.

Facility	Site requirement
Sanitary conveniences (toilets) 	■ Suitable and sufficient toilets should be provided or made available. ■ Toilets should be adequately ventilated and lit and should be clean. ■ Separate toilet facilities should be provided for men and women.
Washing facilities 	■ Sufficient facilities must be available, and include showers if required by the nature of the work. ■ They should be in the same place as the toilets and near any changing rooms. ■ There must be a supply of clean hot (or warm) and cold running water, soap and towels. ■ There must be separate washing facilities provided for men and women unless the area is for washing hands and the face only.

Facility	Site requirement
Clean drinking water 	■ This must be provided or made available. ■ It should be clearly marked by an appropriate sign. ■ Cups should be provided unless the supply of drinking water is from a water fountain.
Changing rooms and lockers 	■ Changing rooms must be provided or made available if operatives have to wear special clothing and if they cannot be expected to change elsewhere. ■ There must be separate rooms for, or separate use of rooms by, men and women where necessary. ■ The rooms must be have seating and include, where necessary, facilities to enable operatives to dry their special clothing and their own clothing and personal effects. ■ Lockers should also be provided.
Rest rooms or rest areas 	■ They should have enough tables and seating with backs for the number of operatives likely to use them at any one time. ■ Where necessary, rest rooms should include suitable facilities for pregnant women or nursing mothers to rest lying down. ■ Arrangements must be made to ensure that meals can be prepared, heated and eaten. It must also be possible to boil water.

ACTIVITY

What facilities are provided at your workplace or place of training?

PROVISION AND USE OF WORK EQUIPMENT REGULATIONS (PUWER) 1997

The Provision and Use of Work Equipment Regulations (PUWER) 1997 place duties on:

■ people and companies who own, operate or have control over work equipment

■ employers whose employees use work equipment.

Work equipment can be defined as any machinery, appliance, apparatus, tool or installation for use at work (whether exclusively or not). This includes equipment which employees provide for their own use at work. The scope of work equipment is therefore extremely wide. The use of work equipment is also very widely interpreted and, according to the HSE, means 'any activity involving work equipment and includes starting, stopping, programming, setting, transporting, repairing, modifying, maintaining, servicing and cleaning.' It includes equipment such as diggers, electric planers, stepladders, hammers or wheelbarrows.

Under PUWER, work equipment must be:

- suitable for the intended use

- safe to use

- well maintained

- inspected regularly.

Regular inspection is important as a tool that was safe when it was new may no longer be safe after considerable use.

Additionally, work equipment must only be used by people who have received adequate instruction and training. Information regarding the use of the equipment must be given to the operator and must only be used for what it was designed to do.

Protective devices, eg emergency stops, must be used. Brakes must be fitted where appropriate to slow down moving parts to bring the equipment to a safe condition when turned off or stopped. Equipment must have adequate means of isolation. Warnings, either by signs or other means such as sounds or lights, must be used as appropriate. Access to dangerous parts of the machinery must be controlled. Some work equipment is subject to additional health and safety legislation which must also be followed.

Employers who use work equipment must manage the risks. ACoPs (see page 9) have been developed in line with PUWER. The ACoPs have a special legal status, as outlined in the introduction to the PUWER ACoP:

> *Following the guidance is not compulsory and you are free to take other action. But if you do follow the guidance you will normally be doing enough to comply with the law. Health and safety inspectors seek to secure compliance with the law and may refer to this guidance as illustrating good practice.*

INDUSTRY TIP

Abrasive wheels are used for grinding. Under PUWER these wheels can only be changed by someone who has received training to do this. Wrongly fitted wheels can explode!

ACTIVITY

All the tools you use for your work are covered by PUWER. They must be well maintained and suitable for the task. A damaged head on a bolster chisel must be reshaped. A split shaft on a joiner's wood chisel must be repaired. Why would these tools be dangerous in a damaged condition? List the reasons.

MANUAL HANDLING OPERATIONS REGULATIONS 1992

Employers must try and avoid manual handling within reason if there is a possibility of injury. If manual handling cannot be avoided then they must reduce the risk of injury by means of a risk assessment.

An operative lifting heavy bricks

LIFTING AND HANDLING

Incorrect lifting and handling is a serious risk to your health. It is very easy to injure your back – just ask any experienced builder. An injured back can be very unpleasant, so it's best to look after it.

Here are a few things to consider when lifting:

- Assess the load. Is it too heavy? Do you need assistance or additional training? Is it an awkward shape?

- Can a lifting aid be used, such as any of the below?

Wheelbarrow

Gin lift

Scissor lift

Kerb lifter

- Does the lift involve twisting or reaching?

- Where is the load going to end up? Is there a clear path? Is the place it's going to be taken to cleared and ready?

How to lift and place an item correctly

If you cannot use a machine, it is important that you keep the correct posture when lifting any load. The correct technique to do this is known as **kinetic lifting**. Always lift with your back straight, elbows in, knees bent and your feet slightly apart.

Kinetic lifting

A method of lifting that ensures that the risk of injury is reduced

Safe kinetic lifting technique

When placing the item, again be sure to use your knees and beware of trapping your fingers. If stacking materials, be sure that they are on a sound level base and on bearers if required.

Heavy objects that cannot easily be lifted by mechanical methods can be lifted by several people. It is important that one person in the team is in charge, and that lifting is done in a co-operative way. It has been known for one person to fall down and the others then drop the item!

CONTROL OF NOISE AT WORK REGULATIONS 2005

Under the Control of Noise at Work Regulations 2005, duties are placed on employers and employees to reduce the risk of hearing damage to the lowest reasonable level practicable. Hearing loss caused by work is preventable. Hearing damage is permanent and cannot be restored once lost.

EMPLOYER'S DUTIES UNDER THE REGULATIONS

An employer's duties are:

■ To carry out a risk assessment and identify who is at risk.

■ To eliminate or control its employees exposure to noise at the workplace and to reduce the noise as far as practicable.

■ To provide suitable hearing protection.

■ To provide health surveillance to those identified as at risk by the risk assessment.

■ To provide information and training about the risks to their employees as identified by the risk assessment.

EMPLOYEES' DUTIES UNDER THE REGULATIONS

Employees must:

■ Make full and proper use of personal hearing protectors provided to them by their employer.

■ If they discover any defect in any personal hearing protectors or other control measures they must report it to their employer as soon as is practicable.

Ear defenders

NOISE LEVELS

Under the Regulations, specific actions are triggered at specific noise levels. Noise is measured in decibels and shown as dB (a). The two main action levels are 80dB (a) and 85dB (a).

Requirements at 80dB (a) to 85dB (a):

■ Assess the risk to operatives' health and provide them with information and training.

■ Provide suitable ear protection free of charge to those who request ear protection.

Requirements above 85dB (a):

■ Reduce noise exposure as far as practicable by means other than ear protection.

■ Set up an ear protection zone using suitable signage and segregation.

■ Provide suitable ear protection free of charge to those affected and ensure they are worn.

Ear plugs

INDUSTRY TIP

The typical noise level for a hammer drill and a concrete mixer is 90 to 100dB (a).

PERSONAL PROTECTIVE EQUIPMENT (PPE) AT WORK REGULATIONS 1992

Employees and subcontractors must work in a safe manner. Not only must they wear the PPE that their employers provide they must also look after it and report any damage to it. Importantly, employees must not be charged for anything given to them or done for them by the employer in relation to safety.

ACTIVITY

Think about your place of work or training. What PPE do you think you should use when working with cement or using a powered planer?

The hearing and respiratory PPE provided for most work situations is not covered by these Regulations because other regulations apply to it. However, these items need to be compatible with any other PPE provided.

The main requirement of the Regulations is that PPE must be supplied and used at work wherever there are risks to health and safety that cannot be adequately controlled in other ways.

The Regulations also require that PPE is:

- included in the method statement

- properly assessed before use to ensure it is suitable

- maintained and stored properly

- provided to employees with instructions on how they can use it safely

- used correctly by employees.

An employer cannot ask for money from an employee for PPE, whether it is returnable or not. This includes agency workers if they are legally regarded as employees. If employment has been terminated and the employee keeps the PPE without the employer's permission, then, as long as it has been made clear in the contract of employment, the employer may be able to deduct the cost of the replacement from any wages owed.

Using PPE is a very important part of staying safe. For it to do its job properly it must be kept in good condition and used correctly. If any damage does occur to an article of PPE it is important that this is reported and it is replaced. It must also be remembered that PPE is a last line of defence and should not be used in place of a good safety policy!

A site safety sign showing the PPE required to work there

The following table shows the type of PPE used in the workplace and explains why it is important to store, maintain and use PPE correctly. It also shows why it is important to check and report damage to PPE.

PPE	Correct use
Hard hat/safety helmet 	Hard hats must be worn when there is danger of hitting your head or danger of falling objects. They often prevent a wide variety of head injuries. Most sites insist on hard hats being worn. They must be adjusted to fit your head correctly and must not be worn back to front! Check the date of manufacture as plastic can become brittle over time. Solvents, pens and paints can damage the plastic too.
Toe-cap boots or shoes  Safety boots / A nail in a construction worker's foot.	Toe-cap boots or shoes are worn on most sites as a matter of course and protect the feet from heavy falling objects. Some safety footwear has additional insole protection to help prevent nails going up through the foot. Toe caps can be made of steel or lighter plastic.
Ear defenders and plugs  Ear defenders Ear plugs	Your ears can be very easily damaged by loud noise. Ear protection will help prevent hearing loss while using loud tools or if there is a lot of noise going on around you. When using earplugs always ensure your hands are clean before handling the plugs as this reduces the risk of infection. If your ear defenders are damaged or fail to make a good seal around your ears have them replaced.
High visibility (hi-viz) jacket 	This makes it much easier for other people to see you. This is especially important when there is plant or vehicles moving in the vicinity.
Goggles and safety glasses   Safety goggles Safety glasses	These protect the eyes from dust and flying debris while you are working. It has been known for casualties to be taken to hospital after dust has blown up from a dry mud road. You only get one pair of eyes, look after them!

PPE	Correct use
Dust masks and respirators  Dust mask Respirator	Dust is produced during most construction work and it can be hazardous to your lungs. It can cause all sorts of ailments from asthma through to cancer. Wear a dust mask to filter this dust out. You must ensure it is well fitted. Another hazard is dangerous gases such as solvents. A respirator will filter out hazardous gases but a dust mask will not! Respirators are rated P1, P2 and P3, with P3 giving the highest protection.
Gloves  Latex glove Nitrile glove  Gauntlet gloves Leather gloves	Gloves protect your hands. Hazards include cuts, abrasions, dermatitis, chemical burns or splinters. Latex and nitrile gloves are good for fine work, although some people are allergic to latex. Gauntlets provide protection from strong chemicals. Other types of gloves provide good grip and protect the fingers.  A chemical burn as a result of not wearing safety gloves
Sunscreen Suncream Melanoma	Another risk, especially in the summer months, is sunburn. Although a good tan is sometimes considered desirable, over-exposure to the sun can cause skin cancer such as melanoma. When out in the sun, cover up and use sunscreen (ie suncream) on exposed areas of your body to prevent burning.
Preventing HAVS 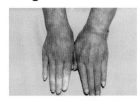	Vibration white finger (VWS) is a symptom of an industrial injury known as HAVS and is caused by using vibrating power tools (such as a hammer drill, vibrating poker and vibrating plate) for a long time. This injury is controlled by limiting the time such power tools are used. For more information see page 31.

ACTIVITY

You are working on a site and a brick falls on your head. Luckily, you are doing as you have been instructed and you are wearing a helmet. You notice that the helmet has a small crack in it. What do you do?

1 Carry on using it as your employer will charge you for a new one, after all it is only a small crack.

2 Take it to your supervisor as it will no longer offer you full protection and it will need replacing.

3 Buy a new helmet because the old one no longer looks very nice.

INDUSTRY TIP

The most important pieces of PPE when using a disc cutter are dust masks, glasses and ear protection.

WORK AT HEIGHT REGULATIONS 2005

The Work at Height Regulations 2005 put several duties upon employers:

- Working at height should be avoided if possible.

- If working at height cannot be avoided, the work must be properly organised with risk assessments carried out.

- Risk assessments should be regularly updated.

- Those working at height must be trained and competent.

- A method statement must be provided.

Operatives working at height as a roof is lifted into place

Several points should be considered when working at height:

- How long is the job expected to take?

- What type of work will it be? It could be anything from fitting a single light bulb, through to removing a chimney or installing a roof.
  - How is the access platform going to be reached? By how many people?
  - Will people be able to get on and off the structure safely? Could there be overcrowding?

- What are the risks to passers-by? Could debris or dust blow off and injure anyone on the road below?

- What are the conditions like? Extreme weather, unstable buildings and poor ground conditions need to be taken into account.

A cherry picker can assist you when working at height

ACCESS EQUIPMENT AND SAFE METHODS OF USE

The means of access should only be chosen after a risk assessment has been carried out. There are various types of access.

Ladders

Ladders are normally used for access onto an access platform. They are not designed for working from except for light, short-duration work. A ladder should lean at an angle of 75°, ie one unit out for every four units up.

Strong upper resting point

Adequate lap on extension ladders

Ground back slope not exceeding 6°

Ground side slope not exceeding 16°, clean and free of slippery algae and moss

Using a ladder correctly

Roof ladder

Resting ladders on plastic guttering can cause it to bend and break

The following images show how to use a ladder or stepladder safely.

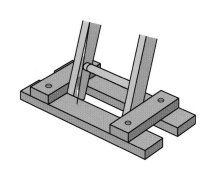

A ladder secured at the base.

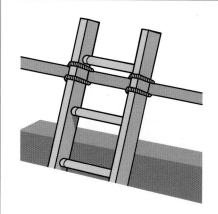

A ladder secured at the top of a platform for working from.

Access ladders should extend 1m above the landing point to provide a strong handhold.

Certain stepladders are unsafe to work from the top three rungs.

Don't overreach, and stay on the same rung.

Grip the ladder when climbing and remember to keep three points of contact.

INDUSTRY TIP

Always complete ladder pre-checks. Check the stiles (the two uprights) and rungs for damage such as splits or cracks. Do not use painted ladders because the paint could be hiding damage! Check all of the equipment including any stays and feet.

Stepladders

Stepladders are designed for light, short-term work.

Working from the side can make stepladders unstable. Do not overreach

Don't stand on the top three steps

Stepladder is fully open

Locked open firm and level on the ground

Using a stepladder correctly

Trestles

This is a working platform used for work of a slightly longer duration.

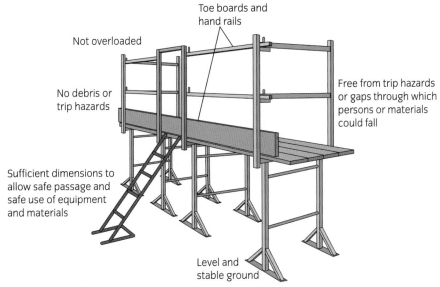

Not overloaded

Toe boards and hand rails

No debris or trip hazards

Free from trip hazards or gaps through which persons or materials could fall

Sufficient dimensions to allow safe passage and safe use of equipment and materials

Level and stable ground

Parts of a trestle

Tower scaffold

These are usually proprietary (manufactured) and are made from galvanised steel or lightweight aluminium alloy. They must be erected by someone competent in the erection and dismantling of mobile scaffolds.

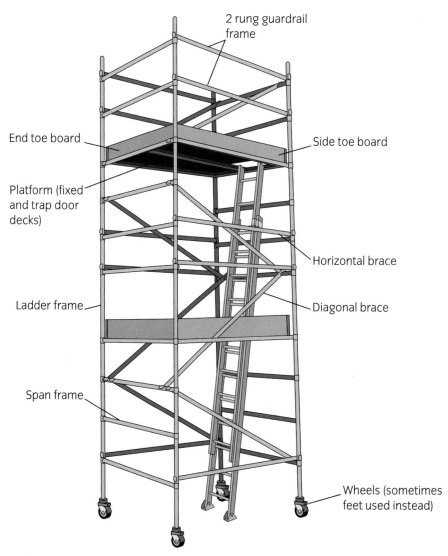

2 rung guardrail frame

End toe board

Side toe board

Platform (fixed and trap door decks)

Horizontal brace

Ladder frame

Diagonal brace

Span frame

Wheels (sometimes feet used instead)

Parts of a tower scaffold

To use a tower scaffold safely:

- Always read and follow the manufacturer's instruction manual.

- Only use the equipment for what it is designed for.

- The wheels or feet of the tower must be in contact with a firm surface.

- Outriggers should be used to increase stability. The maximum height given in the manufacturer's instructions must not be exceeded.

- The platform must not be overloaded.

- The platform should be unloaded (and reduced in height if required) before it is moved.

- Never move a platform, even a small distance, if it is occupied.

Tubular scaffold

This comes in two types:

- independent scaffold has two sets of standards or uprights
- putlog scaffold is built into the brickwork.

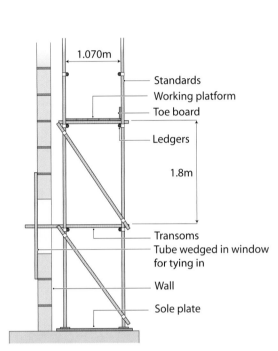

Independent tubular scaffold

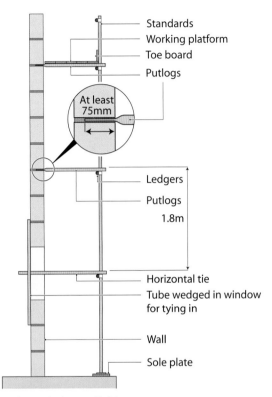

Putlog tubular scaffold

Tubular scaffold is erected by specialist scaffolding companies and often requires structural calculations. Only trained and competent scaffold erectors should alter scaffolding. Access to a scaffold is usually via a tied ladder with three rungs projecting above the step off at platform level.

OUR HOUSE

You have been asked to complete a job that requires gaining access to the roof level of a two-storey building. What equipment would you choose to get access to the work area? What things would you take into consideration when choosing the equipment? Take a look at 'Our House' as a guide for working on a two-storey building.

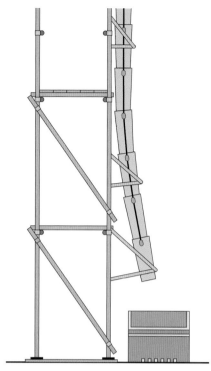

A debris chute for scaffolding

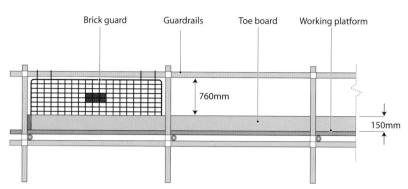

Brick guard   Guardrails   Toe board   Working platform

760mm

150mm

A safe working platform on a tubular scaffold

All scaffolding must:

- not have any gaps in the handrail or toe boards
- have a safe system for lifting any materials up to the working height
- have a safe system of debris removal.

Fall protection devices include:

- harnesses and lanyards
- safety netting
- air bags.

A harness and lanyard or safety netting will stop a person falling too far, leaving them suspended in the air. Air bags (commonly known as 'bouncy castles') are set up on the ground and inflated. If a person falls, they will have a soft landing. Air bags have fallen out of favour somewhat as some operatives use them as an easy way to get off the working platform – not the purpose they were intended for!

A safe scaffolding set up

LIFTING OPERATIONS AND LIFTING EQUIPMENT REGULATIONS (LOLER) 1998

The Lifting Operations and Lifting Equipment Regulations (LOLER) 1998 put responsibility upon employers to ensure that the lifting equipment provided for use at work is:

- strong and stable enough for the particular use and marked to indicate safe working loads
- positioned and installed to minimise any risks
- used safely, ie the work is planned, organised and performed by competent people
- subject to on-going thorough examination and, where appropriate, inspection by competent people.

THE CONTROL OF VIBRATION AT WORK REGULATIONS 2005

Vibration white finger or hand-arm vibration syndrome (HAVS), see page 23, is caused by using vibrating tools such as hammer drills, vibrating pokers or hand held breakers over a long period of time. The most efficient and effective way of controlling exposure to hand-arm vibration is to look for new or alternative work methods which remove or reduce exposure to vibration.

Follow these steps to reduce the effects of HAVS:

■ Always use the right tool for each job.

■ Check tools before using them to make sure they have been properly maintained and repaired to avoid increased vibration caused by faults or general wear.

■ Make sure cutting tools are kept sharp so that they remain efficient.

■ Reduce the amount of time you use a tool in one go, by doing other jobs in between.

■ Avoid gripping or forcing a tool or work piece more than you have to.

■ Encourage good blood circulation by:
  • keeping warm and dry (when necessary, wear gloves, a hat, waterproofs and use heating pads if available)
  • giving up or cutting down on smoking because smoking reduces blood flow
  • massaging and exercising your fingers during work breaks.

Damage from HAVS can include the inability to do fine work and cold can trigger painful finger blanching attacks (when the ends of your fingers go white).

An operative taking a rest from using a power tool

Don't use power tools for longer than you need to

CONSTRUCTION SITE HAZARDS

DANGERS ON CONSTRUCTION SITES

Study the drawing of a building site. There is some demolition taking place, as well as construction. How many hazards can you find? Discuss your answers.

Dangers	Discussion points
Head protection	The operatives are not wearing safety helmets, which would prevent them from hitting their head or from falling objects.
Poor housekeeping	The site is very untidy. This can result in slips trips and falls and can pollute the environment. An untidy site gives a poor company image. Offcuts and debris should be regularly removed and disposed of according to site policy and recycled if possible.
Fire	There is a fire near a building; this is hazardous. Fires can easily become uncontrollable and spread. There is a risk to the structure and, more importantly, a risk of operatives being burned. Fires can also pollute to the environment.

Dangers	Discussion points
Trip hazards	Notice the tools and debris on the floor. The scaffold has been poorly constructed. There is a trip hazard where the scaffold boards overlap.
Chemical spills	There is a drum leaking onto the ground. This should be stored properly – upright and in a lockable metal shed or cupboard. The leak poses a risk of pollution and of chemical burns to operatives.
Falls from height	The scaffold has handrails missing. The trestle working platform has not been fitted with guard rails. None of the operatives are wearing hard hats for protection either.
Noise	An operative is using noisy machinery with other people nearby. The operative should be wearing ear PPE, as should those working nearby. Better still, they should be working elsewhere if at all possible, isolating themselves from the noise.
Electrical	Some of the wiring is 240V as there is no transformer, it's in poor repair and it's also dragging through liquid. This not only increases the risk of electrocution but is also a trip hazard.
Asbestos or other hazardous substances	Some old buildings contain **asbestos** roofing which can become a hazard when being demolished or removed. Other potential hazards include lead paint or mould spores. If a potentially hazardous material is discovered a supervisor must be notified immediately and work must stop until the hazard is dealt with appropriately.

Asbestos

A naturally occurring mineral that was commonly used for a variety of purposes including: **insulation**, fire protection, roofing and guttering. It is extremely hazardous and can cause a serious lung disease known as asbestosis

Insulation

A material that reduces or prevents the transmission of heat

Cables can be a trip hazard on site

Boiler suit

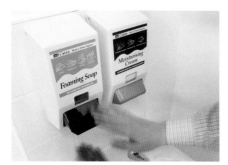

Hand cleaner

PERSONAL HYGIENE

Working in the construction industry can be very physical, and it's likely to be quite dirty at times. Therefore you should take good care with your personal hygiene. This involves washing well after work. If contaminants are present, then wearing a protective suit, such as a boiler suit, that you can take off before you go home will prevent contaminants being taken home with you.

You should also wash your hands after going to the toilet and before eating. This makes it safer to eat and more pleasant for others around you. The following step by steps show a safe and hygienic way to wash your hands.

STEP 1 Apply soap to hands from the dispenser.

STEP 2 Rub the soap into the lather and cover your hands with it, including between your fingers.

STEP 3 Rinse hands under a running tap removing all of the soap from your hands.

STEP 4 Dry your hands using disposable towels. Put the towel in the bin once your hands are dry.

WORKING WITH ELECTRICITY

Electricity is a very useful energy resource but it can be very dangerous. Electricity must be handled with care! Only trained, competent people can work with electrical equipment.

THE DANGERS OF USING ELECTRICAL EQUIPMENT

The main dangers of electricity are:

- shock and burns (a 230V shock can kill)

- electrical faults which could cause a fire

- an explosion where an electrical spark has ignited a flammable gas.

VOLTAGES

Generally speaking, the lower the voltage the safer it is. However, a low voltage is not necessarily suitable for some machines, so higher voltages can be found. On site, 110V (volts) is recommended and this is the voltage rating most commonly used in the building industry. This is converted from 230V by use of a transformer.

110V 1 phase – yellow

230V (commonly called 240V) domestic voltage is used on site as battery chargers usually require this voltage. Although 230V is often used in workshops, 110V is recommended.

410V (otherwise known as 3 phase) is used for large machinery, such as joinery shop equipment.

Voltages are nominal, ie they can vary slightly.

230V 1 phase – blue

BATTERY POWER

Battery power is much safer than mains power. Many power tools are now available in battery-powered versions. They are available in a wide variety of voltages from 3.6V for a small screwdriver all the way up to 36V for large masonry drills.

410V 3 phase – red

The following images are all examples of battery powered tools you may come across in your workplace or place of training.

Battery drill   Battery-powered planer   Battery-powered jigsaw

WIRING

The wires inside a cable are made from copper, which conducts electricity. The copper is surrounded by a plastic coating that is colour coded. The three wires in a cable are the live (brown), which works with the neutral (blue) to conduct electricity, making the appliance work. The earth (green and yellow stripes) prevents electrocution if the appliance is faulty or damaged.

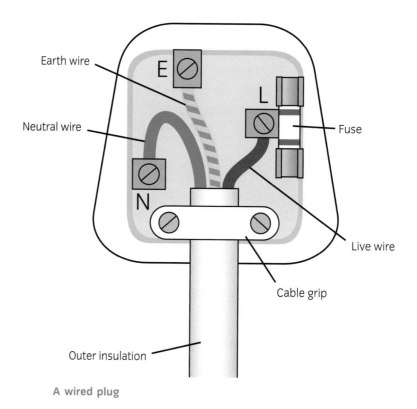

A wired plug

POWER TOOLS AND CHECKS

Power tools should always be checked before use. Always inform your supervisor if you find a fault. The tool will need to be repaired, and the tool needs to be kept out of use until then. The tool might be taken away, put in the site office and clearly labelled 'Do not use'.

Power tool checks include:

- *Look for the powered appliance testing (PAT) label*: PAT is a regular test carried out by a competent person (eg a qualified electrician) to ensure the tool is in a safe electrical condition. A sticker is placed on the tool after it has been tested. Tools that do not pass the PAT are taken out of use.

 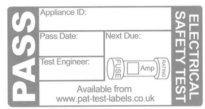

PAT testing labels

- *Cable*: Is it damaged? Is there a repair? Insulation tape may be hiding a damaged cable. Damaged cables must be replaced.

- *Casing*: Is the casing cracked? Plastic casings ensure the tool is double-insulated. This means the live parts inside are safely shielded from the user. A cracked casing will reduce the protection to the user and will require repair.

- *Guards and tooling*: Are guards in place? Is the tooling sharp?

- *Electricity supply leads*: Are they damaged? Are they creating a trip hazard? You need to place them in such a way that they do not make a trip hazard. Are they protected from damage? If they are lying on the floor with heavy traffic crossing them, they must be covered.

- *Use appropriate equipment for the size of the job*: For example, too many splitters can result in a web of cables.

- *Storage*: After use, power tools and equipment should be stored correctly. Tools must be returned to the boxes, including all the guards and parts. Cables need to be wound onto reels or neatly coiled as they can become tangled very easily.

Cable protection

Cable reel

INDUSTRY TIP

Remember, always fully unroll an extension lead before use because it could overheat and cause a fire.

FIRE

Fire needs three things to start; if just one of them is missing there will be no fire. If all are present then a fire is unavoidable:

1 *Oxygen*: A naturally occurring gas in the air that combines with flammable substances under certain circumstances.

2 *Heat*: A source of fire, such as a hot spark from a grinder or naked flame.

3 *Fuel*: Things that will burn such as acetone, timber, cardboard or paper.

The fire triangle

If you have heat, fuel and oxygen you will have a fire. Remove any of these and the fire will go out.

PREVENTING THE SPREAD OF FIRE

Being tidy will help prevent fires starting and spreading. For instance:

- Wood offcuts should not be left in big piles or standing up against a wall. Instead, useable offcuts should be stored in racks.

- Put waste into the allocated disposal bins or skips.

- Always replace the cap on unused fuel containers when you put them away. Otherwise they are a potential source of danger.

- Flammable liquids (not limited to fuel-flammable liquids) such as oil-based paint, thinners and oil must be stored in a locked metal cupboard or shed.

- Smoking around flammable substances should be avoided.

- Dust can be explosive, so when doing work that produces wood dust it is important to use some form of extraction and have good ventilation.

FIRE EXTINGUISHERS AND THEIR USES

You need to know where the fire extinguishers and blankets are located and which fire extinguishers can be used on different fires. The table below shows the different classes of fire and which extinguisher to use in each case.

Class of fire	Materials	Type of extinguisher
A	Wood, paper, hair, textiles	Water, foam, dry powder, wet chemical
B	Flammable liquids	Foam, dry powder, CO_2
C	Flammable gases	Dry powder, CO_2
D	Flammable metals	Specially formulated dry powder
E	Electrical fires	CO_2, dry powder
F	Cooking oils	Wet chemical, fire blanket

Fire blanket

CO_2 extinguisher

Dry powder extinguisher

Water extinguisher

Foam extinguisher

It is important to use the correct extinguisher for the type of fire as using the wrong one could make the danger much worse, eg using water on an electrical fire could lead to the user being electrocuted!

EMERGENCY PROCEDURES

In an emergency, people tend to panic. If an emergency were to occur, such as fire, discovering a bomb or some other security problem, would you know what to do? It is vital to be prepared in case of an emergency.

It is your responsibility to know the emergency procedures on your work site:

- If you discover a fire or other emergency you will need to raise the alarm:
  - You will need to tell a nominated person. Who is this?
  - If you are first on the scene you will have to ring the emergency services on 999.

- Be aware of the alarm signal. Is it a bell, a voice or a siren?

- Where is the assembly point? You will have to proceed to this point in an orderly way. Leave all your belongings behind, they may slow you or others down.

- At the assembly point, there will be someone who will ensure everyone is out safely and will do so by taking a count. Do you know who this person is? If during a fire you are not accounted for, a firefighter may risk their life to go into the building to look for you.

- How do you know it's safe to re-enter the building? You will be told by the appointed person. It's very important that you do not re-enter the building until you are told to do so.

Emergency procedure sign

ACTIVITY

What is the fire evacuation procedure at your workplace or place of training?

SIGNS AND SAFETY NOTICES

The law sets out the types of safety signs needed on a construction site. Some signs that warn us about danger and others tell us what to do to stay safe.

The following table describes five basic types of sign.

Type of sign	Description
Prohibition 	These signs are red and white. They are round. They signify something that must *not* be done.
Mandatory 	These signs are blue. They are round. They signify something that *must* be done.

Type of sign	Description
Caution	These signs are yellow and black. They are triangular. These give warning of hazards.
Safe condition	These signs are green. They are usually square or rectangular. They tell you the safe way to go, or what to do in an emergency.
Supplementary	These white signs are square or rectangular and give additional important information. They usually accompany the signs above.

Case Study: Graham and Anton

An old barn had planning passed in order for it to be converted into a dwelling.

Keith, the contractor, was appointed and the small building company turned up first thing Monday morning.

Graham, the foreman, took a short ladder off the van to access the building's asbestos and slate roof to inspect its condition. The ladder just reached fascia level. As Graham stepped off onto the roof the ladder fell away, leaving him stranded. Luckily for him, Anton the apprentice, who was sitting in the van at the time noticed what had happened and rushed over to put the ladder back up.

While inspecting the whole roof Graham found that the asbestos roof covering was rather old and had become brittle over time, especially the clear plastic roof light sections. It was also clear upon close inspection that the ridge had holes in it and was leaking water. On the slated area of the roof it was noted that many slates were loose and some of them had fallen away leaving the battens and rafters exposed which was leading to severe decay of the timbers.

It was decided that the whole roof needed to be replaced.

- Was the survey carried out safely?

- What accidents could have happened during the survey?

- What could have been done to make the whole operation safer?

- What is the builder's general view of safety?

- How would you carry out the roof work in a safe fashion?

TEST YOUR KNOWLEDGE

Work through the following questions to check your learning.

1 Which of the following must be filled out prior to carrying out a site task?

   a Invoice

   b Bill of quantities

   c Risk assessment

   d Schedule

2 Which of the following signs shows you something you *must* do?

   a Green circle

   b Yellow triangle

   c White square

   d Blue circle

3 Two parts of the fire triangle are heat and fuel. What is the third?

   a Nitrogen

   b Oxygen

   c Carbon dioxide

   d Hydrogen sulphite

4 Which of the following types of fire extinguisher would best put out an electrical fire?

   a CO_2

   b Powder

   c Water

   d Foam

5 Which piece of health and safety legislation is designed to protect an operative from ill health and injury when using solvents and adhesives?

   a Manual Handling Operations Regulations 1992

   b Control of Substances Hazardous to Health (COSHH) Regulations 2002

   c Health and Safety (First Aid) Regulations 1981

   d Lifting Operations and Lifting Equipment Regulations (LOLER) 1998

6 What is the correct angle at which to lean a ladder against a wall?

   a 70°

   b 80°

   c 75°

   d 85°

7 Which are the most important pieces of PPE to use when using a disc cutter?

   a Overalls, gloves and boots

   b Boots, head protection and overalls

   c Glasses, hearing protection and dust mask

   d Gloves, head protection and boots

8 Which of these is not a lifting aid?

   a Wheelbarrow

   b Kerb lifter

   c Gin lift

   d Respirator

9 Which of these is a 3 phase voltage?

   a 410V

   b 230V

   c 240V

   d 110V

10 Above what noise level must you wear ear protection?

   a 75dB (a)

   b 80dB (a)

   c 85dB (a)

   d 90dB (a)

Chapter 2
Unit 101: Principles of building construction, information and communication

Working in the building industry involves more than just the physical construction of buildings such as laying blocks, screwing timber together or soldering pipes. Building is an expensive business and for the work to progress smoothly (and on budget) the work needs to be well organised.

This involves interpreting information such as drawings, specifications and schedules. It also involves calculating quantities and dimensions and knowing how to communicate well with others.

By reading this chapter you will know about:

1 Identifying information used in the workplace.
2 Environmental considerations in relation to construction.
3 Construction of foundations.
4 Construction of internal and external walls.
5 Construction of floors.
6 Construction of roofs.
7 Communicating in the workplace.

TECHNICAL INFORMATION

This section will discuss the three main sources of technical information that are used when constructing buildings:

- working drawings and **specifications**

- schedules

- **bill of quantities**.

These are all essential information and form the contract documents (those that govern the construction of a building). All documentation needs to be correctly interpreted and correctly used. The contract documents need to be looked after and stored (filed) correctly and safely. If documents are left lying around they will become difficult to read and pages may be lost, leading to errors. The contract documents will need to be **archived** at the end of the contract, so they can be referred back to in case of any query or dispute over the work carried out or the materials used.

Specification

A contract document that gives information about the quality of materials and standards of workmanship required

Bill of quantities

A document containing quantities, descriptions and cost of works and resources

Archived

Kept in storage

DRAWING SCALES

It is impossible to fit a full-sized drawing of a building onto a sheet of paper, so it is necessary to **scale** (shrink) the size of the building to enable it to fit. The building has to be shrunk in proportion; this makes it possible to convert measurements on the drawing into real measurements that can be used. Scale rules are made specifically for this purpose.

Scale

The ratio of the size on a drawing to the size of the real thing that it represents

INDUSTRY TIP

How do scale rules work? Let's say we are using a scale of 1:5. That means that what we draw – using the sizes on the scale rule – will be five times smaller on the drawing than the object's actual size. So, a line 30mm long will represent an object 150mm long (30 x 5 = 150).

INDUSTRY TIP

Do not scale from photocopies because these can easily become distorted in the process of photocopying.

INDUSTRY TIP

If a drawing has **dimensions**, use these instead of using a scale rule to take a measurement.

Dimension

A measurement

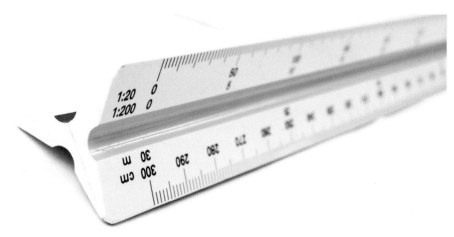

Triangular scale rule

The **British Standards Institute's** BS 1192 (Drawing office practice) gives a range of standard scales that are used for various drawing types and scale rules are manufactured to meet this purpose.

British Standards Institute

The British Standards Institute (BSI) is the UK authority which develops and publishes standards in the UK

SCALES IN COMMON USE

Scale	Use
1:1	Full size (used for rods)
1:2 1:5 1:10	Building details
1:20 1:50 1:100 1:200	Plans, elevations and sections
1:200 1:500 1:1250	Site plans
1:1250 1:2500	Location plans

The documents these scales are used for are described on pages 49–51.

ACTIVITY

Work out the following:

Scale size	Scale	Actual size
10mm	1:10	100mm
25mm	1:20	a)
b)	1:50	300mm
50mm	1:200	c)

Answers: a) 500mm, b) 6mm, c) 10m

DATUM POINTS

Heights of buildings and the relative heights of components within the building are calculated from a common **datum point**. Datum points are determined by transferring a known fixed height from a bench mark. There are two types of datum point:

■ A permanent Ordnance bench mark (OBM) is a given height on an Ordnance Survey map. This fixed height is described as a value, eg so many metres above sea level (as calculated from the average sea height at Newlyn, Cornwall).

■ A temporary bench mark (TBM) is set up on site.

Datum point

A fixed point or height from which reference levels can be taken. The datum point is used to transfer levels across a building site. It represents the finished floor level (FFL) on a dwelling

Ordnance and temporary bench marks

ACTIVITY

Find your local OBM or your site TBM.

BASIC DRAWING SYMBOLS (HATCHINGS)

Standard symbols, also known as hatching symbols, are used on drawings as a means of passing on information simply. If all the parts of a building were labelled in writing, the drawing would soon become very crowded. Additionally, it is important to use standard symbols so that everyone can read them and it means the same to everyone. The following images are just some of the standard symbols used.

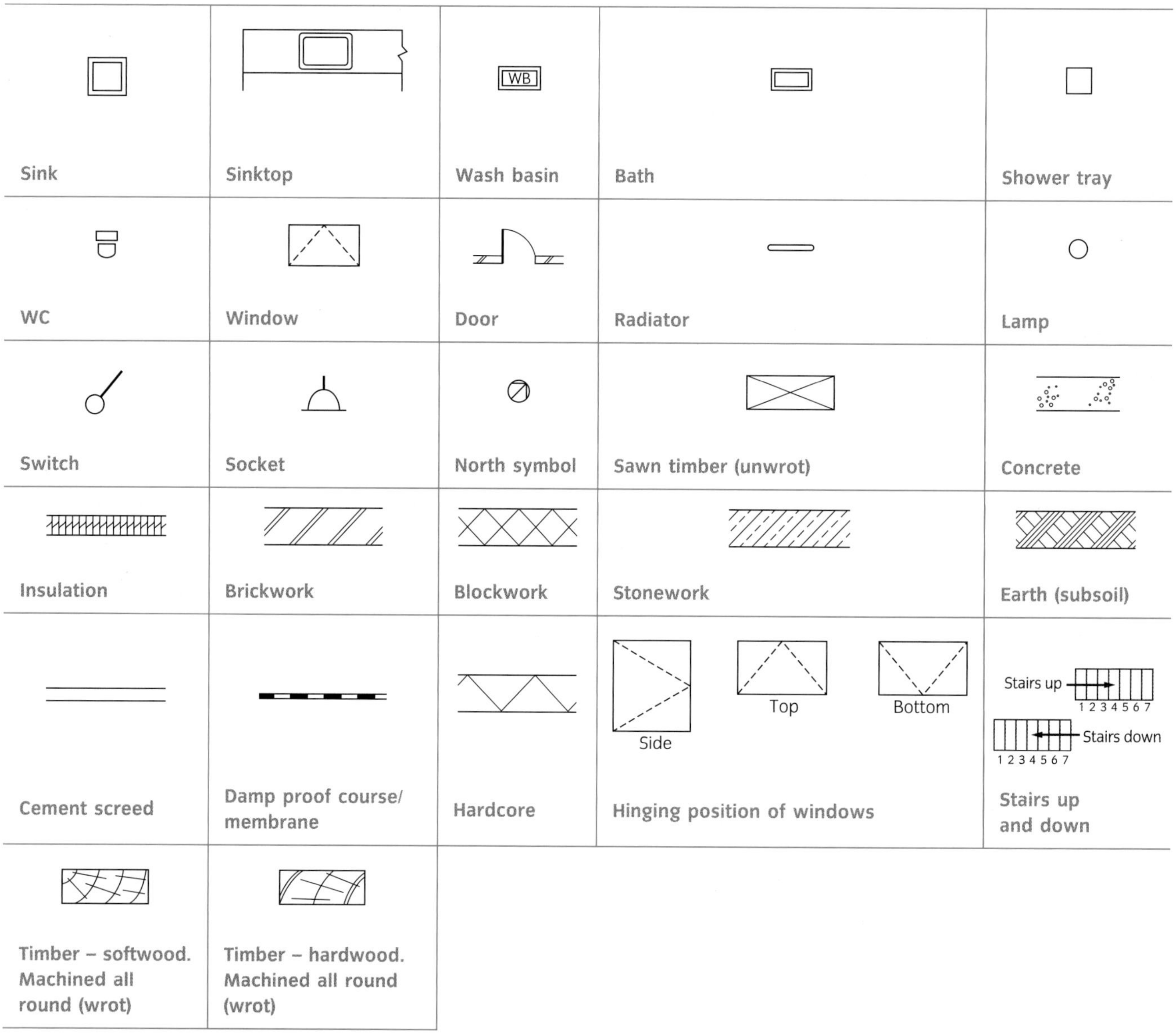
Sink
Sinktop
WB
Wash basin
Bath
Shower tray
WC
Window
Door
Radiator
Lamp
Switch
Socket
North symbol
Sawn timber (unwrot)
Concrete
Insulation
Brickwork
Blockwork
Stonework
Earth (subsoil)
Cement screed
Damp proof course/ membrane
Hardcore
Side
Top
Bottom
Hinging position of windows
Stairs up
1 2 3 4 5 6 7
Stairs down
1 2 3 4 5 6 7
Stairs up and down
Timber – softwood. Machined all round (wrot)
Timber – hardwood. Machined all round (wrot)

INFORMATION SOURCES

Type of drawing	Description
Location drawings	Usually prepared by an **architect** or **architectural technician**. Show the location of the building plot, position of the building and areas within the building. Location drawings covers all of the drawings in this table.
Location plans 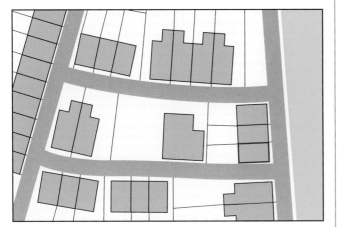 Scale 1:1250	Show the proposed development in relation to its surrounding properties. The scales used are 1:1250 or 1:2500. Very little detail is available from this type of plan. The direction North is usually shown.
Block plans (Site plans) 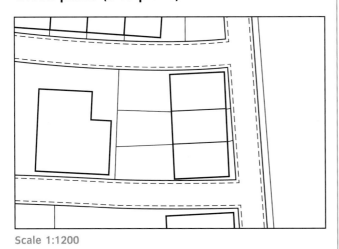 Scale 1:1200	Show the plot in more detail, with drain runs, road layouts and the size and position of the existing building (and any extensions proposed) in relation to the property boundary. A scale of 1:500 or 1:200 is used.

Architect

A trained professional who designs a structure and represents the client who wants the structure built. They are responsible for the production of the working drawings. They supervise the construction of buildings or other large structures

Architectural technician

A draftsperson who works in an architectural practice

Type of drawing	Description
Floor plans 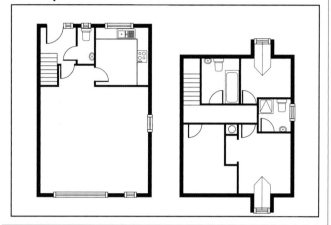	Show the positioning of walls, size of rooms along with the positioning of elements within the building such as units.
Elevations 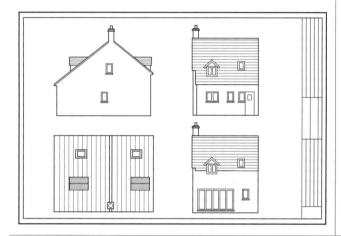	Show a building from a particular side and show the positioning of features such as doors and windows.
Sections 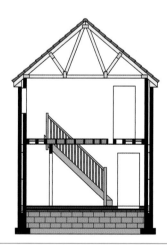	Show in greater detail what the section of a component looks like and how it might fit in relation to another component. A typical example would be a cross-section of a window showing the size of the features and how it fits together. Using these drawings it is possible to determine the positions of rooms, windows, doors, kitchen units and so on. Elevations are shown. These drawings are more detailed, and are often scaled to provide construction measurements. Scales used are 1:200, 1:100 and 1:50, 1:10, 1:5 and 1:1. A scale of 1:1 is full size.

Type of drawing	Description
Construction drawings (Detail drawings) Detail showing typical exterior corner detail External walls / Exterior cladding / Breather membrane paper Exterior cladding / Wall plate stud / Breather membrane paper / Vapour control membrane on the inside of the timber frame	Show details of construction, normally as a cross-section.

SPECIFICATIONS

A specification accompanies the working drawings. They give further information that cannot be shown on the drawings. The drawings need to be clear and not covered in notes. A specification would include information such as:

- the colour of paint required

- a specific timber species

- the brick type required

- the plaster finish required.

They are prepared by construction professionals such as architects and building services engineers. They can be produced from previous project specifications, in-house documents or master specifications such as the National Building Specification (NBS). The NBS is owned by the Royal Institute of British Architects (RIBA).

Example of a specification

COMPONENT RANGE DRAWINGS

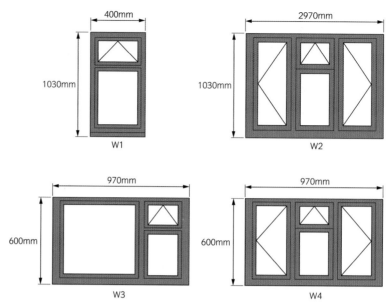

Component range drawing of windows

A component range drawing shows the range of components available from a manufacturer. It includes:

- sizes available

- coding for ordering purposes

- availability (whether it can be bought off-the-shelf or if pre-ordering is required).

Availability is particularly important when planning delivery dates. Schedules reference this type of drawing.

SCHEDULES

A schedule is used to record repeated design information that applies to a range of components or fittings, such as:

- windows

- doors

- kitchen units

- joinery fittings.

A schedule is mainly used on bigger sites where there are multiples of several designs of houses, with each type having different components and fittings. It avoids the wrong component or fitting being put in the wrong house.

A schedule is usually used in conjunction with a component range drawing and a floor plan.

In a typical plan, the doors and windows are labelled D1, D2, W1, W2 etc. These components would be included in the schedule, which would provide additional information on them, for example see the following schedule.

Master Internal Door Schedule							
Ref:	Door size	S.O. width	S.O. height	Lintel type	FD30	Self closing	Floor level
D1	838x1981	900	2040	BOX	Yes	Yes	GROUND FLOOR
D2	838x1981	900	2040	BOX	Yes	Yes	GROUND FLOOR
D3	762x1981	824	2040	BOX	No	No	GROUND FLOOR
D4	838x1981	900	2040	N/A	Yes	No	GROUND FLOOR
D5	838x1981	900	2040	BOX	Yes	Yes	GROUND FLOOR
D6	762x1981	824	2040	BOX	Yes	Yes	FIRST FLOOR
D7	762x1981	824	2040	BOX	Yes	Yes	FIRST FLOOR
D8	762x1981	824	2040	N/A	Yes	No	FIRST FLOOR
D9	762x1981	824	2040	BOX	Yes	Yes	FIRST FLOOR
D10	762x1981	824	2040	N/A	No	No	FIRST FLOOR
D11	686x1981	748	2040	N/A	Yes	No	SECOND FLOOR
D12	762x1981	824	2040	BOX	Yes	Yes	SECOND FLOOR
D13	762x1981	824	2040	100 HD BOX	Yes	Yes	SECOND FLOOR
D14	686x1981	748	2040	N/A	No	No	SECOND FLOOR

Example of a schedule

BILL OF QUANTITIES

A bill of quantities is produced by the quantity surveyor and describes everything that is required for the job based on the drawings, specification and schedules. A bill of quantities contains the following information:

- *Preliminaries*: General information including the client and architect, details of the work and descriptions of the site.

- *Preambles*: Like the specification, this outlines the quality and description of materials and workmanship, etc.

- *Measured quantities*: A description of how each task and material is to be measured, with measurements in metres (linear and square), hours, litres, kilogrammes and the number of components required.

The completed document is sent out to contractors who will then price the work and enter the costs into the blank spaces. The bill of quantities ensures that all the contractors are pricing for the job using the same information.

BILL OF QUANTITIES

(Assuming Civil Engineering Standard Method of Measurement (CESSM3) is used.)

Number	Item description	Unit	Quantity	Rate	Amount £	p
	CLASS A: GENERAL ITEMS					
	Specified Requirements					
	Testing of Materials					
A250	Testing of recycled and secondary aggregates	sum				
	Information to be provided by the Contractor					
A290	Production of Materials Management Plan	sum				
	Method Related Charges					
	Recycling Plant / Equipment					
A339.01	Mobilise; Fixed	sum				
A339.02	Operate; Time-Related	sum				
A339.03	De-mobilise; Fixed	sum				
	CLASS D: DEMOLITION AND SITE CLEARANCE					
	Other Structures					
D522.01	Other structures; Concrete;	sum				
D522.02	Grading / processing of demolition material to produce recycled and secondary aggregates	m³	70			
D522.03	Disposal of demolition material offsite	m³	30			
	CLASS E: EARTHWORKS					
	Excavation Ancillaries					

Bill of quantities

WORK SCHEDULES

It is very important indeed that the progress of work is planned out. A work schedule or programme of work is an easy way of showing what work is to be carried out and when. This is usually shown in the form of a bar chart called a gantt chart. The chart lists the tasks that need to be done on the left-hand side and shows a timeline across the top. The site manager or trade supervisors can quickly tell from looking at this chart:

- if work is keeping to schedule

- what materials, equipment, labour are required

- when they are required.

Materials very often have a lead-in time and so cannot be delivered immediately. These need to be ordered and delivered at the correct time. Labour planning is also required as the trades may be working elsewhere when needed.

	Time (days)						
Task	**1**	**2**	**3**	**4**	**5**	**6**	**7**
Prepare the ground	▓	▓					
Spread foundations			▓	▓			
Lay cables for services				▓	▓		
Build walls up to DPC						▓	▓
Proposed time in green							

Gantt chart

INDUSTRY TIP

Use of a planning document such as a gantt chart will reduce waste and ensure effective use of labour.

CALCULATING QUANTITIES FOR MATERIALS

Calculations are required throughout the building process. It is important that these calculations are accurate, as mistakes can be very expensive. Several factors can have an impact on cost. Underestimating:

- the amount of materials required

- how much they cost

- how long it will take to complete a job

can lose the company a lot of money. It could also lead to the company gaining a bad reputation for not being able to complete a job on time and in budget.

Materials are usually better priced if bought in bulk, whereas a buy-as-you go approach can cost more. Consider these points when buying materials:

- Is there sufficient storage room for delivered materials?

- Is there a risk of the materials being damaged if there is nowhere suitable to store them or if they are delivered too early?

- Will it be a problem to obtain the same style, colour or quality of product if they are not all ordered at the same time?

- Will over-ordering cause lots of wastage ?

These and many other considerations will help determine when and in what quantity materials are ordered.

Some wastage is unavoidable. Allowances must be made for wastage, eg cut bricks that cannot be re-used, short ends of timber, partly full paint cans. Up to 5% waste is allowed for bricks and blocks and 10% for timber and paint.

It may be that all the materials are ordered by the office or supervisory staff, but you still need to know how to recognise and calculate material requirements. Deliveries have to be checked before the delivery note is signed and the driver leaves. Any discrepancies in the type or quantity of materials, or any materials that have arrived damaged, must be recorded on the delivery note and reported to the supervisor. Any discrepancies will need to be followed up and new delivery times arranged.

You must be able to identify basic materials and carry out basic calculations. You will often have to collect sufficient materials to carry out a particular operation. Being able to measure accurately will mean you can make the most economic use of materials and therefore reduce waste.

Deliveries must be checked before signing the delivery note

UNITS OF MEASUREMENT

The construction industry uses metric units as standard; however you may come across some older measures called imperial units.

Units for measuring	Metric units	Imperial units
Length	millimetre (mm) metre (m) kilometre (km)	inch (in) or " eg 6" (6 inches) foot (ft) or ' eg 8' (8 foot)
Liquid	millilitre (ml) litre (l)	pint (pt)
Weight	gramme (g) kilogramme (kg) tonne (t)	pound (lb)

ACTIVITY

Look online to find out:
- What other imperial units are still commonly used?
- How many millimetres are there in an inch?
- How many litres are there in a gallon?

Units for measuring	Quantities	Example
Length	There are 1000mm in 1m. There are 1000m in 1km.	1mm x 1000 = 1m 1m x 1000 = 1km 6250mm can be shown as 6.250m 6250m can be shown as 6.250km
Liquid	There are 1000ml in 1l.	1ml x 1000 = 1l
Weight	There are 1000g in 1kg. There are 1000kg in 1t.	1g x 1000 = 1kg 1kg x 1000 = 1t

CALCULATIONS

Four basic mathematical operations are used in construction calculations.

ADDITION

The addition of two or more numbers is shown with a plus sign (**+**).

> **Example 1**
>
> A stack of bricks is 3 bricks long and 2 bricks high. It contains 6 bricks.
>
> $$3 + 3 = 6$$
>
> More examples:
>
> $$5 + 2 = 7$$
> $$19 + 12 = 31$$
> $$234 + 105 = 339$$

Pallet of bricks

SUBTRACTION

The reduction of one number by another number is shown with a minus sign (**–**).

> **Example 1**
>
> A pallet containing 100 bricks is delivered on site, but you only need 88 bricks. How many are left over?
>
> $$100 - 88 = 12$$
>
> More examples:
>
> $$5 - 2 = 3$$
> $$19 - 12 = 7$$
> $$234 - 105 = 129$$

MULTIPLICATION

The scaling of one number by another number is shown with a multiplication sign (**x**).

Example 1

A stack of bricks is 3 bricks long and 2 bricks high. It contains 6 bricks.

$$3 \times 2 = \mathbf{6}$$

More examples:

$$19 \times 12 = \mathbf{228}$$

$$234 \times 10 = \mathbf{2340}$$

$$234 \times 105 = \mathbf{24{,}570}$$

In the last example, the comma (,) is used to show we are in the thousands. In words we would say, twenty four thousand, five hundred and seventy.

DIVISION

Sharing one number by another number in equal parts (how many times it goes into the number) is shown with a division sign (÷).

Example 1

$$5 \div 2 = \mathbf{2.5}$$

$$36 \div 12 = \mathbf{3}$$

$$600 \div 4 = \mathbf{150}$$

LINEAR LENGTH

Linear means how long a number of items would measure from end to end if laid in a straight line. Examples of things that are calculated in linear measurements are:

- skirting board

- lengths of timber

- rope

- building line

- wallpaper.

Skirting boards are calculated using linear measurements

We use this form of measurement when working out how much of one of the materials listed above we need, eg to find out how much

A joiner measuring a room

Perimeter

The distance around an object or room

skirting board is required for a room. First, we need to measure the **perimeter** (sides) of a room. To find the linear length we add the length of all four sides together. This can be done in two ways: adding or multiplying.

Example 1

A site carpenter has been asked how many metres of skirting are required for the rooms below.

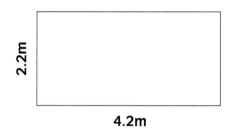

They can add all the sides together:
$$2.2 + 4.2 + 2.2 + 4.2 = 12.8m$$

Or, they can multiply each side by 2, and add them together:
$$(2.2 \times 2) + (4.2 \times 2) = 12.8m$$

Either way, **12.8m** is the correct answer.

Example 2

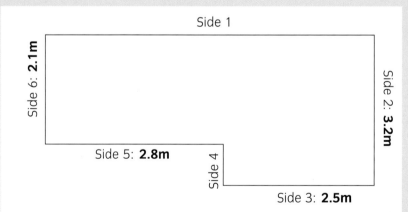

To work out the perimeter of this room we need to add all the sides together. In this example each side has been given a reference number, so all we need to do is add all the sides together, like this:

side 1 (side 3 + side 5) + side 2 + side 3 + side 4 (side 2 - side 6) + side 5 + side 6

Now, let's show the working out: 2.8 + 2.5 + 3.2 + 2.5 + 3.2 - 2.1 + 2.8 + 2.1 = 17m

The amount of skirting board required is **17m**.

Now let's put some door openings in. This symbol represents an opening.

Example 3

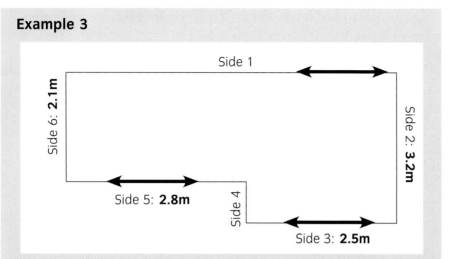

On side 1 there is an opening 0.9m wide, on side 3 there is an opening 1.5m wide and on side 5 there is an opening 2.1m wide.

We know from Example 2 that the perimeter of the room is 17m. We now need to remove the openings. Skirting board will not be needed for the openings.

Step 1

Add together the lengths of the three combined openings:

0.9 + 1.5 + 2.1 = 4.5m

Step 2

Deduct this from 17m:

17 − 4.5 = 12.5m

The linear length of skirting board required is 12.5m.

Step 3

However, this calculation does not take into account any waste. We would normally add 10% extra to allow for waste:

12.5 + 10% = 12.5 + 1.25 = 13.75m

The total amount of skirting board required is **13.75m**.

PERCENTAGES

An easy way to find a percentage (%) of a number is to divide the number by 100 and then multiply it by the percentage you require.

> **For example:**
>
> Increase 19m by 12%
>
> 19 ÷ 100 = 0.19
>
> 0.19 x 12 = 2.28
>
> 19 + 2.28 = 21.28m
>
> Total required **21.28m**.

AREA

Floors

The structured layers of a building, eg ground floor, first floor, second floor

To find out how much material is required to cover a surface such as a **floor** or wall you need to calculate its area. Area is the measurements of a two dimensional surface, eg the surface of floors, walls, glass or a roof.

To find the area of a surface you need to multiply its length by its width (L x W) or one side by the other. This will give you an answer which is expressed in square units (^{2}). For example, mm², m² or km².

> **Example 1**
>
> A bricklayer has been asked to work out the area of the floors below.
>
>
>
> Side 1: **2.2m**   Side 2: **4.4m**
>
> side 1 x side 2 = floor area
>
> 2.2 x 4.4 = 9.68m²
>
> The total floor area is **9.68m²**.

Irregularly shaped areas can be calculated by breaking up the area into sections that can be worked out easily, and then adding them together.

Example 2

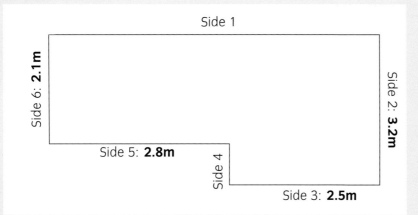

Irregularly shaped rooms can be split into sections to calculate the area

Step 1

Divide the area into two parts, and then calculate the area of each part. The easiest way to do this is to divide it into two smaller sections:

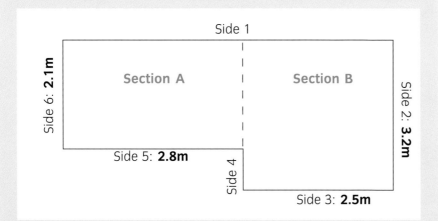

Step 2

Work out the area of section A and section B:

section A: 2.1 x 2.8 = 5.88m²

section B: 2.5 x 3.2 = 8m²

Step 3

Add the areas of section A and section B together:

section A + section B = total floor area

5.88 + 8 = 13.88m²

The total floor area is **13.88m²**.

A tiler tiling a floor

ACTIVITY

Find the area of the following measurements:

1 2.1m x 2.4m
2 0.9m x 2.7m
3 250mm x 3.4m

Answers: 1) 5.04m, 2) 2.43m, 3) 0.85m

Now let's say the floor requires tiling. The tiler needs to calculate the number of floor tiles required.

Example 3

The size of each floor tile is 305mm x 305mm. We can also show this as 0.305m x 0.305m.

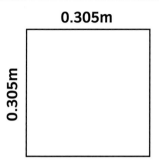

How many floor tiles are required for the floor area in Example 2? The total floor area is 13.88m².

Step 1

Calculate the area of one tile. As the floor area is given in m², we need to calculate the size of the tile in the same unit, ie m².

0.305 x 0.305 = 0.093m²

Step 2

Now you need to divide the total floor area by the area of one tile to find out the total number tiles required.

total floor area ÷ area of one tile = total number of tiles

13.88 ÷ 0.093 = 149.247 tiles

This number is rounded up to the next full tile, so a total of 150 floor tiles are required.

Step 3

However, this total does not allow for any waste.

Add 5% to allow for waste:

150 + 5% = 158 tiles (to the next full tile)

Let's look at the working out:

150 ÷ 100 = 1.5 tiles (this is 1%)

1.5 x 5 = 7.5 tiles (this is 5%)

5% of 150 tiles, rounded up to the next full tile, is 8 tiles.

Therefore **158 tiles** are required.

AREA OF A TRIANGLE

Sometimes you will be required to work out an area that includes a triangle.

A decorator measuring a room

Example 1

A painter has been asked to work out how much paint will be needed to paint the front of this house.

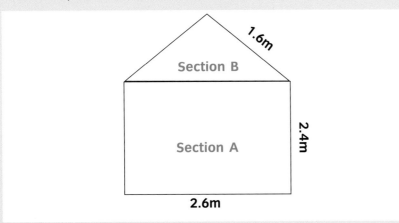

Step 1

Divide the area up into a rectangular section (section A) and a triangular section (section B).

Step 2

Find the area of section A:

2.4 x 2.6 = 6.24m²

The area of section A is 6.24m².

Step 3

Find the area of section B

The area of a triangle can be found by multiplying the base by the height, then dividing by 2.

(base x height) ÷ 2 = area

2.6 x 1.6 = 4.16

4.16 ÷ 2 = 2.08m²

The area of section B is 2.08m².

Step 4

area of section A + area of section B = total wall area

6.24 + 2.08 = 8.32m²

The total wall area is **8.32m²**.

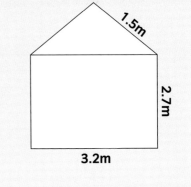

Now let's look at the simple triangle below. It has three sides, A, B and C. Pythagorean theorem tells us that in a right-angled triangle the **hypotenuse** is equal to the sum of the square of the lengths of the two other sides, in other words a² + b² = c². In this example the hypotenuse is side C.

Using the Pythagorean theorem we can work out the length of any side.

Hypotenuse

The longest side of a right-angled triangle. It is always opposite the right angle

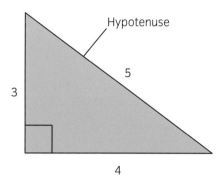

The hypotenuse

INDUSTRY TIP

If a triangle has a small square in the corner, this shows you the corner is a right angle.

Example 1

If side A is 3m long and side B is 4m long, what is the length of side C?

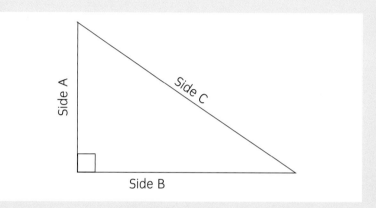

3 x 3 = 9

4 x 4 = 16

9 + 16 = 25

√25 = 5

(√ means square root, or a number that is multiplied by itself, in this case 5 x 5 = 25)

Side C is **5m** long.

Example 2

A joiner has been asked to work out the length of a roof (side C).

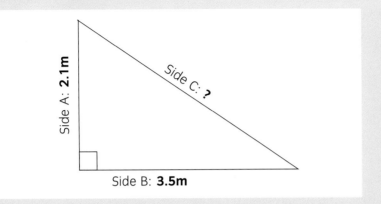

2.1 x 2.1 (side A) = 4.41

3.5 x 3.5 (side B) = 12.25

4.41 + 12.25 = 16.66

√16.66 = 4.08m

The length of side C is **4.08m**.

Example 3

A bricklayer needs to find the rise of a roof (side A).

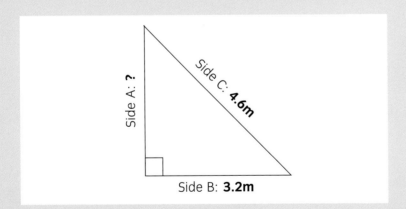

3.2 x 3.2 (side B) = 10.24

4.6 x 4.6 (side C) = 21.16

21.16 − 10.24 = 10.92

√10.92 = 3.30m

The length of side A is **3.3m**.

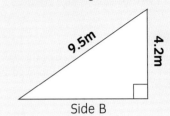
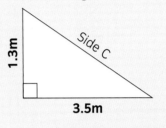

PERIMETERS AND AREAS OF CIRCLES

Circumference

The distance around the edge of a circle

Diameter

The length of a straight line going through the centre of a circle connecting two points on its circumference

Sometimes you are required to find the perimeter or **circumference** of a circle.

circumference of a circle = π x **diameter**

$$C = \pi d$$

π (or 'pi') is the number of times that the diameter of a circle will divide into the circumference.

π = 3.142

This is equal to the number of diameters in one revolution of a circle. It is the same for any sized circle.

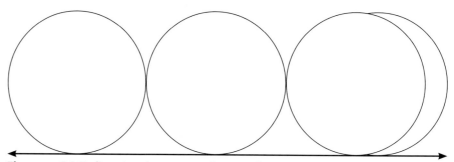

There are 3.142 diameters in one complete revolution

Example 1

A joiner is making a circular window that has a diameter of 600mm. Its circumference is:

0.600 x 3.142 = **1.885m**

The diameter of a circle from a given circumference is:

diameter = circumference ÷ π

Example 2

A window has a circumference of 2.250m. Its diameter is:

2.250 ÷ 3.142 = **0.716m** (or 716mm)

Radius

The length of a line from the centre to a point on the circumference of a circle. It is exactly half the length of the diameter

The area of a circle is found by:

area of a circle = π x **radius**² (radius is equal to half the diameter)

Example 3

A painter needs to paint a circle that is 1.2m in diameter and is required to find the area of the circle to enable them to order the correct quantity of paint.

1.2 ÷ 2 = **0.600** (the radius)

3.142 x 0.600² = **1.13m²**

VOLUME

The volume of an object is the total space it takes up, eg a tin of paint, a foundation for a wall or the capacity of a concrete mixer, and is shown as m³ (cubic metres). To find the volume of an object you must multiply length by width by height.

volume = length x width x height

Example 1

Each side of this cube is 1m. The total space it takes up is 1m³

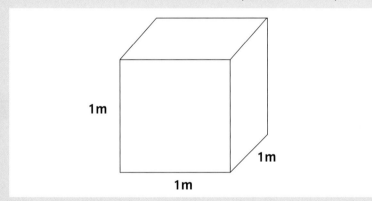

1m x 1m x 1m = **1m³**

Example 2

A bricklayer has been asked to work out how many m³ of **concrete** is required for a strip foundation. The size of the foundation is 3.2m long, 0.600m wide and 0.900m deep.

length x width x height = volume

3.2 x 0.600 x 0.900 = 1.728m³

The volume of concrete needed for the strip foundation is **1.728m³**.

A bricklayer taking levels

Concrete

Composed of cement, sand and stone, of varying size and in varying proportions

To work out the volume of a cylinder:

$$volume = \pi r^2 h \; (\pi \times r^2 \times h)$$

Example 3

A joiner has a tin of presevative and needs to know its volume. The tin has a diameter of 250mm and a height of 700mm.

$\pi r^2 h \; (\pi \times r^2 \times h)$ = volume

The radius (r) is half the diameter:

$250 \div 2 = 125mm$

$3.142 \times 0.125^2 \times 0.700 = 0.034m^3$

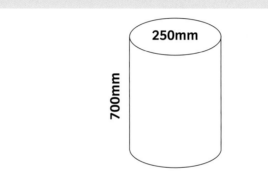

The volume of the tin of paint is **0.034m³**.

COMMUNICATION

Good communication is vital to the smooth running of any building project.

Communication involves sharing thoughts, information and ideas between people. For communication to be effective, information must be:

- given in a clear way
- received without misunderstanding.

It has been said that to be a good communicator it is just as important to be a good listener as it is to be a good speaker! Good communication leads to a safer and more efficient workplace, not to mention helping to maintain a pleasant working environment.

Most sites will have policies and procedures in place that govern the chain of command and communication between supervisory staff and workers.

WRITTEN COMMUNICATION

There are many methods of communication within the building industry. In this chapter we have discussed drawings, schedules and specifications etc. The architect uses these methods to communicate details about the building to the team who will **tender** for and erect the building.

Communication is usually electronic via email (with or without attachments) or through intranet sites. Drawings are very commonly distributed in electronic formats which are printed on to paper when required. Messages are often given via text.

Sometimes communication will be via a memorandum (memo), a written form of communication with a message.

Site rules, risk assessments and method statements (see Chapter 1) communicate safety information.

Tender

The process of supplying the client with a fixed quotation for the work

INDUSTRY TIP

Messages that are passed on by word of mouth are open to interpretation, so written messages often can be more clear.

SITE PAPERWORK

Communication on site is aided by the use of paperwork and without it no building site could operate. It is an important method of communication between operatives and supervisory staff, builders, architects and clients.

Type of paperwork	Description
Timesheet	Used to record the hours completed each day, and is usually the basis on which pay is calculated. Timesheets also help to work out how much the job has cost in working hours, and can give information for future estimating work when working up a tender.

Timesheet

Employer: CPF Building Co.	Employee Name: Louise Miranda	Week starting: 17/6/13

Date: 21/6/13

Day	Job/Job Number	Start Time	Finish Time	Total Hours	Overtime
Monday	Penburthy, Falmouth 0897	9am	6pm	8	
Tuesday	Penburthy, Falmouth 0897	9am	6pm	8	
Wednesday	Penburthy, Falmouth 0897	8.30am	5.30pm	8	
Thursday	Trelawney, Truro 0901	11am	8pm	8	2
Friday	Trelawney, Truro 0901	11am	7pm	8	1
Saturday	Trelawney, Truro 0901	9am	1pm	4	
Totals				40	7

Employee's signature:_____

Supervisor's signature: _____

Type of paperwork	Description
Job sheet **CPF Building Co** **Job sheet** **Customer name:** Henry Collins **Date:** 9/12/13 **Address:** 57 Green St Kirkham London **Work to be carried out** Finishing joint work to outer walls **Instructions** Use weather struck and half round	Gives details of a job to be carried out, sometimes with material requirements and hours given to complete the task.
Variation order **Confirmation notice** **Architect's instruction** **CPF Building Co** **Variation order** **Project Name:** Penburthy House, Falmouth, Cornwall **Reference Number:** 80475 **Date:** 14/11/13 **From: :** _____ **To:** _____ **Reason for change:** **Tick** Customer requirements ☑ Engineer requirements ☐ Revised design ☐ **Instruction:** Entrance door to be made from Utile hardwood with brushed chrome finished ironmongery (changed from previous detail, softwood with brass ironmongery). Signature _____	Sometimes alterations are made to the contract which changes the work to be completed, eg a client may wish to move a door position or request a different brick finish. This usually involves a variation to the cost. This work should not be carried out until a variation order and a confirmation notice have been issued.

Type of paperwork	Description
Requisition order	Filled out to order materials from a supplier or central store. These usually have to be authorised by a supervisor before they can be used.

CPF Building Co
Requisition order

Supplier Information: Construction Supplies Ltd   **Date:** 9/12/13

Contract Address/Delivery Address: Penburthy House, Falmouth, Cornwall

Tel number: 0207294333

Order Number: 26213263CPF

Item number	Description	Quantity	Unit/Unit Price	Total
X22433	75mm 4mm gauge countersunk brass screws slotted	100	30p	£3
YK7334	Brass cups to suit	100	£5	£500
V23879	Sadikkens water based clear varnish	1 litre	£20.00	£20.00
Total:				£523.00

Authorised by: Denzil Penburthy

Delivery note	Accompanies a delivery. Goods have to be checked for quantity and quality before the note is signed. Any discrepancies are recorded on the delivery note. Goods that are not suitable (because they are not as ordered or because they are of poor quality) can be refused and returned to the supplier.

Construction Supplies Ltd
Delivery note

Customer name and address:
CPF Building Co
Penburthy House
Falmouth
Cornwall

Delivery Date: 16/12/13
Delivery time: 9am

Order number: 26213263CPF

Item number	Quantity	Description	Unit Price	Total
X22433	100	75mm 4mm gauge countersunk brass screws slotted	30p	£3
YK7334	100	Brass cups to suit	£5	£500
V23879	1 litre	Sadikkens water based clear varnish	£20	£20

Subtotal	£530.00
VAT	20%
Total	£636.00

Discrepancies: ....

Customer Signature: ....

Print name: ....

Date: ....

Type of paperwork	Description
Delivery record 	Every month a supplier will issue a delivery record that lists all the materials or hire used for that month.
Site diary 	This will be filled out daily. It records anything of note that happens on site such as deliveries, absences or occurrences, eg delay due to the weather.
Invoices 	Sent by the supplier. They list the services or materials supplied along with the price the contractor is requested to pay. There will be a time limit in which to pay. Sometimes there will be a discount for quick payment or penalties for late payment.

Davids & Co
Monthly delivery record

Customer name and address:	Customer order date:
CPF Building Co Penburthy House Falmouth Cornwall	28th May 2013

Item number	Quantity	Description	Unit Price	Date Delivered
BS3647	2	1 ton bag of building sand	£60	3/6/13
CM4324	12	25kg bags of cement	£224	17/6/13

Customer Signature: ....

Print name: ....

Date: ....

VERBAL COMMUNICATION

Often, managers, supervisors, work colleagues and trades communicate verbally. This can be face to face or over a telephone. Although this is the most common form of communication, it is also the most unreliable.

Mistakes are often made while communicating verbally. The person giving the information might make an error. The person receiving the information might misunderstand something because the information is unclear or it is noisy in the background, or because they later forget the details of the conversation.

Confusion can be minimised by recording conversations or by using a form of written communication. If there is a record it can be used for future reference and help to clear up any misunderstandings.

TAKING A TELEPHONE MESSAGE

It is a good idea to take down details of telephone calls and many companies provide documentation for this purpose. When taking a message it is important to record the following details:

- *Content*: This is the most important part of the message – the actual information being relayed. Take and write down as many details as possible.

- *Date and time*: Messages are often time sensitive, and may require an urgent response.

- *Who the message is for*: Ensure the person gets the message by giving it to them or leaving it in a place where they will find it.

- *Contact name and details*: Write down the name of the person leaving the message, and how to get back to them with a response.

UNACCEPTABLE COMMUNICATION

When communicating, it is very important to stay calm. Think about what you are going to say. An angry word will often encourage an angry response. However, keeping calm and composed will often diffuse a stressful situation. A shouting match rarely ends with a good or productive result.

There are several types of communication that are unacceptable and could result in unemployment. Unacceptable communication includes:

- aggressive communication such as swearing or using inappropriate hand gestures

An operative taking notes during a phone call

- racist or sexist comments or gestures

- showing prejudice against people with disabilities.

This type of behaviour shows a lack of respect for others and does not create a safe or pleasant working environment. It will also give your company a poor image if customers see or hear this behaviour. Acting in this way is likely to result in trouble for you and your employer and could even result in a **tribunal** and loss of employment.

Tribunal

A judgement made in court

KNOWLEDGE OF THE CONSTRUCTION INDUSTRY AND BUILT ENVIRONMENT

Buildings come in a wide variety of types in relation to appearance and methods of construction. Despite the variety of buildings, they all have design features in common. In this section we will discuss various parts of buildings and their purpose.

We will also discuss sustainable construction – how buildings can be designed to sit better within the environment, with lower pollution levels and energy requirements both during the building process and when in use.

A house with solar panels

FOUNDATIONS

Foundations serve as a good base on which to put the building. They need to be capable of carrying the weight of the building and any further load that may be put upon it. These are known as **dead loads** and **imposed loads**.

Foundations must be designed to resist any potential movement in the ground on which the building will sit. Ground conditions can vary widely. Soil samples are taken to help decide on the type of foundation to use. This usually takes the form of bore holes dug or drilled around the site. These samples are sent away for testing in a laboratory. The results will identify:

- the soil condition (clay or sandy)

- the depth of the soil

- the depth of the water table

- if any contaminations are present.

The soil condition is important: clay soil drains poorly and can move if it gets waterlogged or dries out completely. Sandy soils drain very well, but can become unstable. A foundation that is suitable for the ground type and load of the building will be designed.

Foundation

Used to spread the load of a building to the sub soil

Dead load

The weight of all the materials used to construct the building

Imposed load

Additional loads that may be placed on the structure, eg people, furniture, wind and snow

INDUSTRY TIP

The type of foundation to be used will usually be decided by the architect and a structural engineer and will be the result of tests.

TYPES OF FOUNDATION

Different types of structures, such as detached houses, high rise and low rise buildings, will all require different types of foundation.

High rise building

Low rise building

Detached house

STRIP FOUNDATIONS

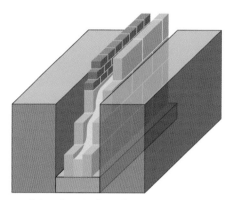

Traditional strip foundation

A strip foundation is the traditional type of foundation used for residential developments (ordinary houses). It is formed by digging a trench to the required width and depth as determined by the soil conditions and the weight of the structure. It is either filled with concrete or a layer of concrete is poured into the bottom. This layer must be a minimum of 150mm thick and is commonly 225mm thick.

Footings are brought up to the level of the **damp proof course** (DPC) using concrete blocks or bricks. These are set out from the centre of the strip of concrete in order to spread the weight evenly. A variety of specialist bricks and blocks are used for this purpose. They need to be able to resist water penetration and therefore frost damage.

Footings

The substructure below ground level. These are projecting courses at the base of a wall

Damp proof course (DPC)

A layer of plastic that prevents damp rising up through a wall needs to be positioned at least 150mm above ground level

Engineering brick

Trench block

It can be economical to fill the trench up to the top with concrete rather than build a substructure – this is known as trench fill. Sometimes it is necessary to build on the edge of the concrete – this is known as an eccentric foundation.

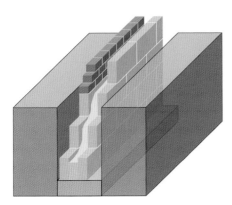

Eccentric foundation

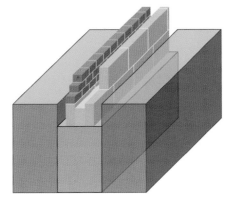

Trench fill foundation

WIDE STRIP FOUNDATIONS

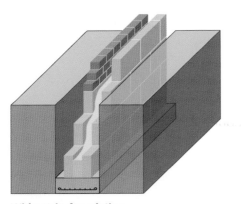

Wide strip foundation

A wide strip foundation is very similar to strip foundation in most of its aspects. The main difference between the two is that a wide strip foundation has steel reinforcements placed within the concrete. The steel gives considerably more strength to the foundation and enables greater loads to be placed on it. Without the steel reinforcements the foundation would need to be much deeper and would need vast amounts of concrete.

PAD FOUNDATIONS

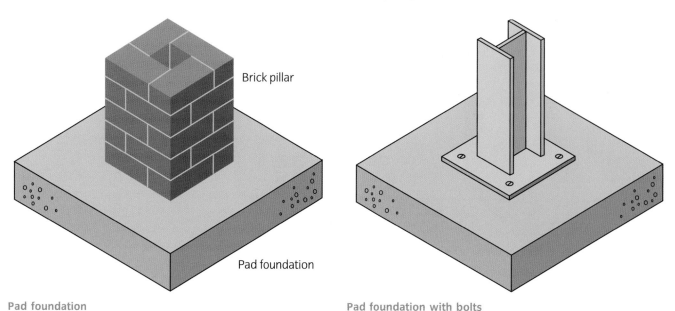

Brick pillar

Pad foundation

Pad foundation

Pad foundation with bolts

A pad foundation is used to support a point load such as a column in a steel-framed building. This type of foundation often has bolts set into the top ready for fixing the steel.

PILE FOUNDATIONS

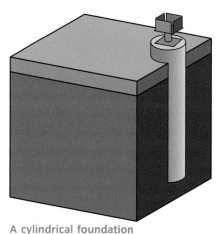

A cylindrical foundation

Deep piles are used to transfer the load through unsuitable soil layers into the harder layers of ground below, even down to rock if required (known as end bearing). Some piles use **friction** to provide support. This is known as skin friction. Tall buildings (and especially narrow buildings such as chimneys or towers) have large lateral forces due to side winds and pile foundations resist these forces well.

INDUSTRY TIP

Foundations are made from concrete. Concrete is made from fine and coarse aggregate (crushed stone) and cement mixed with water. Water reacts with the cement causing it to harden and lock the aggregates together. Concrete is very strong under compression (when weight is put upon it) but is weak when it is pulled (put under tension); therefore steel rods are cast into it to make it stronger.

Friction

Resistance between the surface of the concrete foundation and the soil around it

RAFT FOUNDATIONS

A raft foundation is often laid over an area of softer soil that would be unsuitable for a strip foundation. A raft foundation is a slab of concrete covering the entire base of the building; it spreads the weight of the building over a wider area but still maintains a deeper base around the load bearing walls.

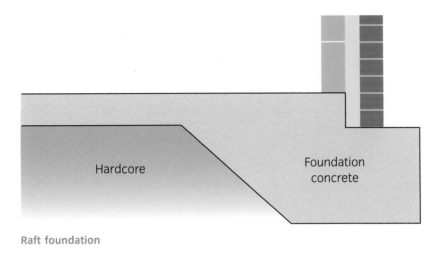

Hardcore

Foundation concrete

Raft foundation

FLOORS

Floors can be divided into two main categories:

- ground floors
- upper floors.

Floors are required to be load bearing, and there is a wide variety of construction methods depending on the type of building and potential load that will be imposed upon the floor. Floors also may need to prevent:

- heat loss
- transfer of sound
- moisture penetration.

GROUND FLOORS

These may be either solid ground floors or suspended floors.

SOLID FLOORS

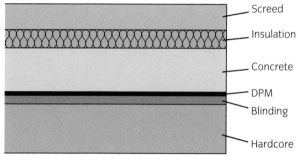

Screed
Insulation
Concrete
DPM
Blinding
Hardcore

Concrete floor

Hardcore

A mixture of crushed stone and sand laid and compacted to give a good base for the concrete

Damp proof membrane (DPM)

An impermeable layer that prevents damp coming up through the floor. A layer of sand known as blinding is placed below the DPM to prevent any sharp stones below piercing the membrane when the concrete is poured

Insulation

Materials used to retain heat and improve the thermal value of a building, may also be used for managing sound transfer

Solid concrete floors are laid upon **hardcore** and have a **damp proof membrane** (DPM) built into them to prevent damp coming up through the floor. **Insulation** is also laid into the floor to reduce heat loss. It is important that the insulation is not affected by the high water content of the wet concrete when being poured.

Steel reinforcement can also be used within the concrete to increase strength and reduce cracks.

HOLLOW AND SUSPENDED FLOORS

Upper floors, and some ground floors, are suspended or hollow meaning that instead of resting on the ground beneath, the load is transferred via beams to the walls. Two types of beam used are Posibeam and I-beam. Timber joists are usually covered with either chip board or solid timber floor boards.

Concrete with steel reinforcement

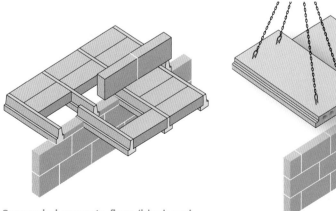

Suspended concrete floor (block and beam)

Pre-cast floor

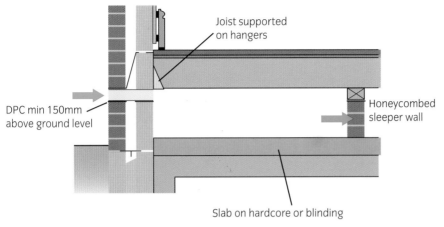

Joist supported on hangers

DPC min 150mm above ground level

Honeycombed sleeper wall

Slab on hardcore or blinding

Suspended wood floor

Posibeam

I-beam

UPPER FLOORS

In most domestic dwellings timber floor joists are used following the same principle as timber ground floors, while in large commercial and industrial buildings solid concrete floors are used.

INDUSTRY TIP

Timber joists normally run across the shortest span.

WALLS

Walling for a building can usually be divided in two categories:

- external
- internal.

Walling can be load or non-load bearing. Load bearing walls carry the weight of the floors and roof and transfer this weight down to the foundations. A non-load bearing wall carries no weight.

Lintel

A horizontal member for spanning an opening to support the structure above

Bond

The arrangement or pattern of laying bricks and blocks to spread the load through the wall, also for strength and appearance

Solid wall

Walls of a thickness of one brick and greater

Cavity wall

Walling built in two separate skins (usually of different materials) with a void held together by wall ties

Walls often have openings in them, eg doors and windows, which will weaken them if they are not constructed correctly. Openings require support (via a **lintel** or arch) across the top to give the wall support and **bond** it together.

EXTERNAL WALLING

External walls need to:

- keep the elements (wind and rain) out of the building

- look good

- fit into the surrounding landscape.

Several methods of construction are used for external walling. Common construction methods are:

- **solid wall**

- **cavity wall**

- timber framing.

SOLID WALL

Solid wall

INDUSTRY TIP

Remember, cement will give chemical burns so use the correct PPE while using and mixing it.

ACTIVITY

What are the walls in the building you are sitting in made from? Why do you think these materials were chosen? What are the advantages or disadvantages of these materials?

Many older traditional buildings have solid walls made from brick, block or stone, see the following table. Solid walls have the disadvantage of being more easily penetrated by damp. Older solid walls are often upgraded by having insulating and waterproofing layers applied to the outside of the wall.

Material used	Description
Bricks 	A very traditional building material made from fired clay, calcium-silicate or concrete. A standard sized brick is 215mm × 102.5mm × 65mm.
Blocks 	These are made of either concrete (crushed stone and cement) or a light-weight cement mixture. They are much bigger than a brick, and are available in various sizes. The most commonly used size is 440mm x 215mm x 100mm. Wider blocks are used for walls where a higher strength or improved sound insulation is required.
Stone 	A natural building material, which varies widely in use and appearance from area to area. Stone may be cut to a uniform size before use or used in its quarried state.
Mortar 	This is used between bricks, blocks and stones to bind them together and increase the strength of the wall. It is a mixture of soft sand and cement mixed with water and other additives if required, eg **plasticiser**, colouring or **lime**. It is important that the strength of the mortar is correct for the type of material that is being used to construct the wall. If the mortar has too much cement in the mix it will be so strong it will not allow movement in the walling due to settlement, and the bricks could crack resulting in the wall needing to be rebuilt. Mortars are mixed to a ratio of materials, eg 1:6. The first number is always the proportion of cement with the second being the proportion of sand. A typical mix ratio for masonry walling is 1:5.

Plasticiser

An additive that is used to make the mortar more pliable and easier to work with

Lime

A fine powdered material traditionally used in mortar

CAVITY WALL

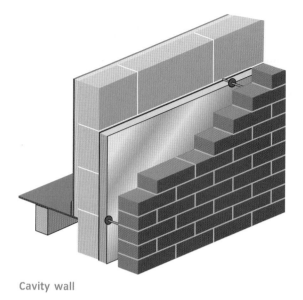

Cavity wall

ACTIVITY

State the minimum performance standards required to meet current building regulations.

ACTIVITY

Find out the current minimum width of cavity allowed.

Leaves

The two walls or skins that make up a cavity wall to comply with current building regulations

Building regulations

A series of documents that set out legal requirements for the standards of building work

The most common type of external walling used today is cavity wall construction.

Cavity walls are two masonry walls built side by side to form an inner and outer leaf (sometimes called skins). The **leaves** are held together with wall ties. These ties are made from rust and rot proof material and are built in as the walls are being constructed. The cavity is partially filled with insulation (typically fibreglass batts or polystyrene boards) as required by the **building regulations**. This reduces heat loss and saves energy.

The inner leaf usually carries any loads from the roof and floors down to the foundations and has a decorative finish on the inside, typically plaster which is either painted or papered. The outer leaf resists the elements and protects the inside of the building.

TIMBER FRAMING

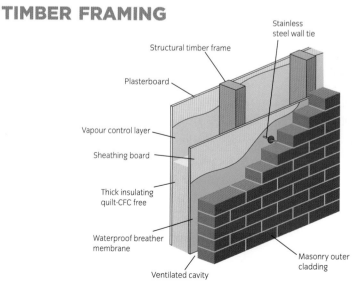

Timber frame wall

Timber framing is both a traditional and modern method of building. Traditional buildings using timber framing were made mostly from oak with various in-fills such as brick or plaster to form the walls. Modern timber frame homes are generally built from softwood and have an outer skin of masonry or are clad with timber or plaster to waterproof the structure. Oak framing, as a traditional building method, is becoming increasingly popular again.

Elizabethan oak frame

PREFABRICATED WALLS

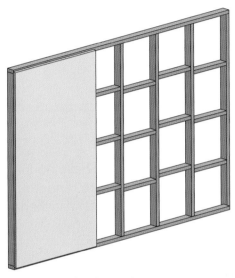

Prefabricated wall panel

There are a variety of prefabricated products available, generally made in a factory and then transported to site to be erected. These products enable quick and easy building. Often the **services** are pre-installed.

Services

Those provided by the utility companies, eg gas, electric and water

INTERNAL WALLING

Internal walling can be load or non-load bearing. Internal partitions divide large internal spaces into smaller rooms.

Internal partitions can be made from studwork or masonry. Studwork partitions consist of studs (which can be made from timber or metal) covered with a sheet material (usually plasterboard).

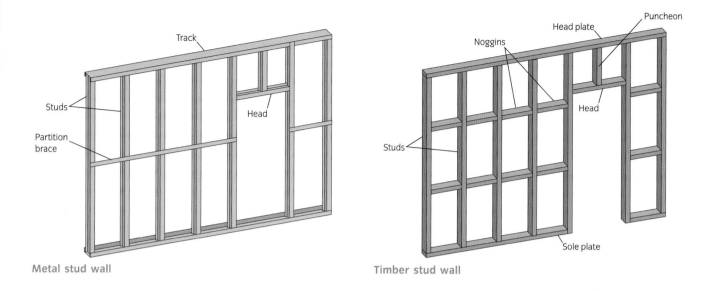

Metal stud wall

Timber stud wall

WALL FINISHES

External walls made from brick usually have no further finishes added while walls made from blocks are rendered. This is a covering of sand and cement mortar which is then finished with masonry paint.

Internal walls are most often plastered with a thin layer of gypsum plaster over plasterboard; this gives a very smooth hardwearing finish which is then usually finished with emulsion paint or papered coverings.

It is important to **size** new plaster to give a good base before applying further coverings of paint or paper coverings. This first coat of paint or paste is usually thinned down by 10% with clean water.

Size

To apply a watered down or mist-coat of paint or paste to new plaster

ROOFS

Roofs are designed to protect the structure below by keeping the weather out. As heat rises, the roof must be well insulated to prevent heat loss and improve the energy efficiency of the building.

TYPES OF ROOFS

Roofs come in a wide variety of designs as the following pictures show.

Pitched roof

Flat roof

ROOF COMPONENTS

Roofs are commonly covered with slates or tiles. Slates are a natural product. Slate is a type of mineral that can be split into thin sheets. Artificial cement fibre slates are also available. Tiles can be made from clay or concrete.

Slate

Cement fibre slate

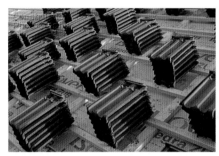

Roof tiles

A felt is laid below the roofing material to provide additional protection in case some water gets through the tiles.

Flashings are commonly made from lead and are used to provide waterproofing at joints where roofing materials meet walls and around chimneys.

Flashing providing waterproofring

Flashing around a chimney

SERVICES

Buildings contain services such as:

- water

- electricity

- gas supplies.

Additionally, waste such as sewage and water run-off have to be considered.

WATER

Water is brought into a building using pipes. Supply pipes used are usually made of plastic, with internal domestic plumbing being made from plastic or copper. Plumbing is installed using a variety of fittings including tees, elbows, and reducers. Bathrooms, kitchens and most heating systems require plumbing.

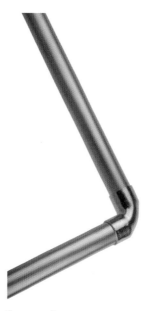

Copper pipe

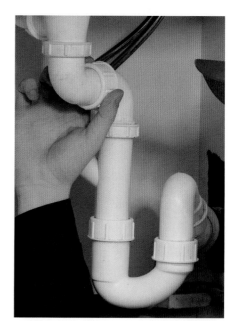

Plastic pipe

Pipe fittings

Not only is water carried into a building, it is also taken away. Rainwater run-off is collected into gutters and taken away via downpipes and drains and returned to the ground or stored for later use.

Rainwater gutter flowing down pipes and into drain

SEWAGE

Sewage is taken away from the building via drains and is disposed of either into a sewer or into a septic tank/sewage treatment plant.

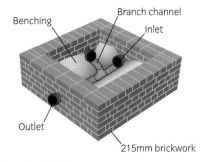

Benched drain

Septic tank

Sewage treatment plant

ELECTRICITY

Electricity is an important service provided to buildings. It powers lighting and heating. It is brought into a building through cables.

Electricity cables, switches and socket

Gas pipework to boiler

ACTIVITY

What services are being used in the building you are sitting in? How are they brought into the building?

GAS

Gas is brought into a building using pipes. Gas powers heating systems and provides fuel for cooking.

OTHER SERVICES

Other services that are installed include telephone systems and other data cables for broadband and entertainment systems.

SUSTAINABILITY

Our planet is a fixed size. Fossil fuels, eg oil and coal, which we take from the ground are not infinite, ie they will run out one day. However, the wind, the sun and the tides will always be there. These are sustainable sources of energy.

Building materials can be sustainable if they are chosen carefully. For example, the process of manufacturing concrete uses a lot of fuel and produces a lot of carbon dioxide (a gas that some say is damaging the climate).

On the other hand, trees absorb carbon dioxide as they grow, look nice and the timber they produce is an excellent building material. However, some timber is harvested from rainforests without thought for the surrounding environment or are harvested to such an extent that certain species are close to extinction. Managed forests where trees are replanted after harvesting provide a sustainable source of timber.

Here are some questions to consider regarding sustainability in construction.

MATERIALS

- How far have the materials been brought? Locally sourced materials do not have to be transported far, thus reducing fuel use.

- Are the materials sustainably sourced? Has the timber come from a managed forest or has it come from a rainforest with no regard to the environment?

- Have the materials been manufactured with the minimum of energy and waste?

DESIGN

Is there an alternative design that can be used that uses more sustainable materials? For example, a timber frame instead of concrete block or brick.

The table below shows some sustainable materials:

Material	Image
Straw bales	
Cob (soil)	
Timber	 Redwood Spruce Oak
Bamboo	

ENERGY EFFICIENCY

Energy is expensive and is only going to get more expensive. As the population increases more and more energy will be required. This needs to come from somewhere and its production can be damaging to the environment. The less power a building uses the better and if it can produce its own that is a bonus. Energy saving measures can save a lot of power consumption.

INSULATION

Light, air-filled materials tend to have better thermal insulation properties than heavy, dense materials. This means that heat cannot easily pass from one side to another and so if these materials are used in a building it will require less heating during the winter and will remain cooler during the summer.

The following drawing shows how much heat a typical home loses through different parts of the property. Better insulation will reduce the amount of heat lost.

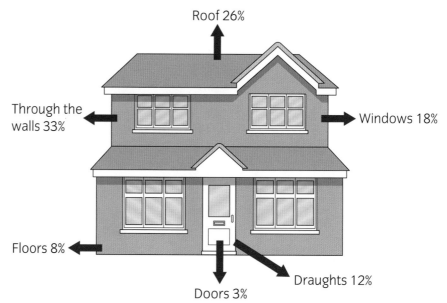

Sources of heat loss from a house

OUR HOUSE

What insulation has been used in the building you are sitting in? Is the building energy efficient? Is it cold? Does it take a lot of heating? Take a look at 'Our House' and identify the insulation measures used there.

The table below shows some examples of insulation:

Type of insulation	Description
Blue jean and lambswool 	Lambswool is a natural insulator. Blue jean insulation comes from recycled denim.
Fibreglass/Rockwool™ 	This is made from glass, often from old recycled bottles or mineral wool. It holds a lot of air within it and therefore is an excellent insulator. It is also cheap to produce. It does however use up a fair bit of room as it takes a good thickness to comply with building regulations. Similar products include plastic fibre insulation made from plastic bottles and lambswool.
PIR (polyisocyanurate) 	This is a solid insulation with foil layers on the faces. It is lightweight, rigid and easy to cut and fit. It has excellent insulation properties. Polystyrene is similar to PIR. Although it is cheaper, its thermal properties are not as good.
Multifoil 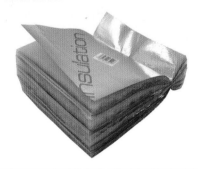	A modern type of insulation made up of many layers of foil and thin insulation layers. These work by reflecting heat back into the building. Usually used in conjunction with other types of insulation.
Double glazing and draught proofing measures 	The elimination of draughts and air flows reduces heat loss and improves efficiency.

MAKING BETTER USE OF EXISTING AND FREE ENERGY

SOLAR POWER

The sun always shines and during the day its light reaches the ground (even on cloudy days). This energy can be used. A simple use of this is to allow sunlight to enter a building. With a little thought in design, light can reach deep into a building via roof lights and light tunnels. This means that internal artificial lighting requirements are reduced, therefore saving energy.

Solar panels can generate hot water or electricity, and once the cost of installation has been covered the energy they produce is totally free.

Solar panel

A panel that absorbs sun rays to generate electricity or hot water

Solar panels

HEAT SOURCE AND RECOVERY

Humans give off a fair bit of energy as they go through a normal day (eg body heat, heat given off by hairdryers, cookers, refrigerators and other activities) and this can be conserved. Modern air-conditioning systems take the heat from stale air and put it into the fresh air coming in.

Heat can be taken from the ground and even the air outside.

WIND POWER

Wind power is becoming more widespread. However some people feel that wind turbines are damaging the visual environment as they spoil the appearance of the countryside. Individuals will have their own opinion on whether wind power is a good thing or not as there are many considerations to be taken into account.

Wind turbine

WATER POWER

Water is another source of power, whether that be hydro-electric (water from dams turning turbines) or wave power which is currently under development.

BIOMASS HEATING

Biomass heating (using wood and other non-fossil fuels) is also becoming more popular as these systems can heat water efficiently as well as heat rooms, and of course a well-insulated building does not require a lot of heating.

ENERGY EFFICIENT GOODS AND APPLIANCES

Energy efficient electrical goods (eg low energy light bulbs) and appliances (eg dishwashers, fridges and washing machines) which use a reduced amount of power and less water are available.

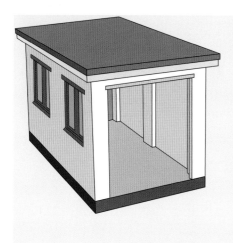

Case Study: Kayleigh

Kayleigh is to build a small single garage at the rear of a house. It must be big enough to accommodate an estate car and give enough room to allow the user to get out and walk around the car. The garage has two windows, an up-and-over door at the front and a flat roof. She has been asked to provide a plan of this garage for the client.

Draw this garage to a scale that will fit onto an A4 piece of paper. Include the window openings, the door, the thickness of the walls (which will be single block) and the piers.

Work through the following questions to check your learning.

1 What is the perimeter of this room?

Side 1: **2.5m**
Side 2: **5m**

a 5m

b 7m

c 15m

d 17m

2 A message that is passed on by word of mouth rather than in writing is

a Open to interpretation

b Very accurate

c Easy to understand if shouted

d Easily remembered

3 What is a component drawing?

a A plan of the whole building, floor by floor

b A section through a part of the structure

c An elevation of the walls

d A detail in a room

4 What is the foundation type shown?

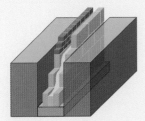

a Strip

b Pile

c Raft

d Pad

5 What is the foundation type shown?

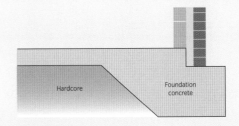

Hardcore   Foundation concrete

a Strip

b Pile

c Raft

d Pad

6 What is the component shown?

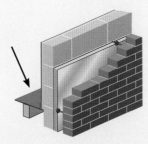

a Damp proof membrane

b Strip foundation

c Damp proof course

d Raft foundation

7 Which **one** of the following materials has the best thermal insulation properties?

a Brick

b Concrete

c Glass

d Polystyrene

8 Concrete sets because it contains

a Aggregate

b Sand

c Hardcore

d Cement

9 A flat roof has a pitch of less than

   a   8°

   b   10°

   c   12°

   d   15°

10 Load bearing walls transmit weight down to the

   a   Foundations

   b   Floors

   c   Roof

   d   Windows

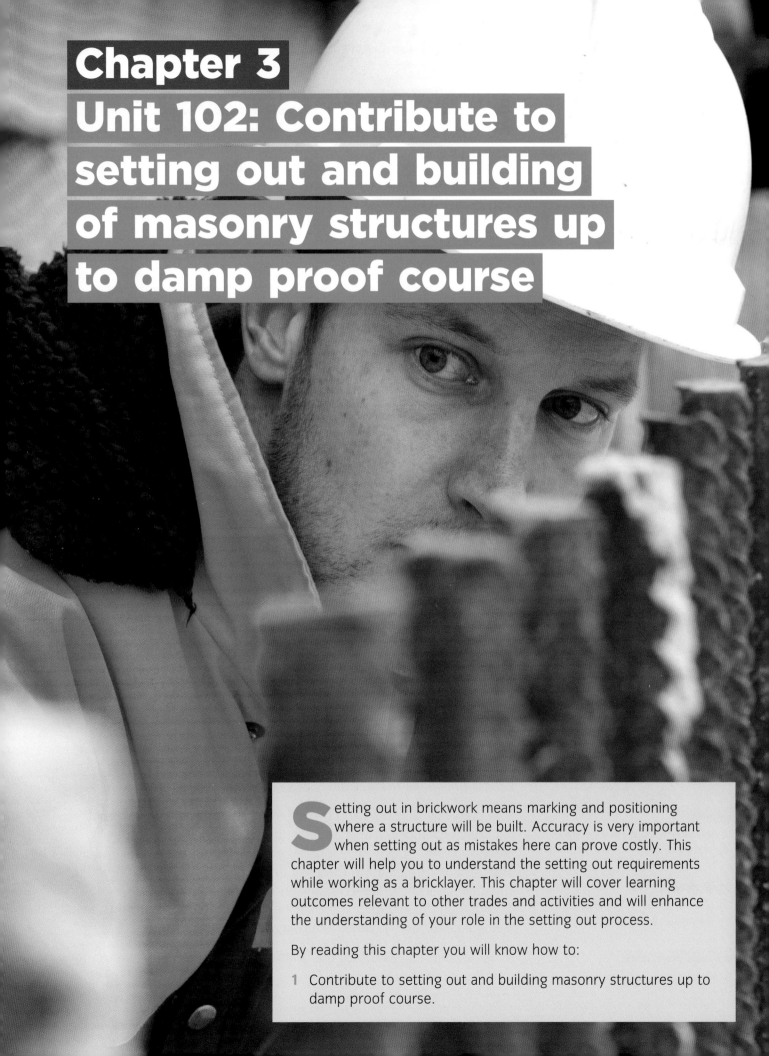

Chapter 3
Unit 102: Contribute to setting out and building of masonry structures up to damp proof course

Setting out in brickwork means marking and positioning where a structure will be built. Accuracy is very important when setting out as mistakes here can prove costly. This chapter will help you to understand the setting out requirements while working as a bricklayer. This chapter will cover learning outcomes relevant to other trades and activities and will enhance the understanding of your role in the setting out process.

By reading this chapter you will know how to:

1 Contribute to setting out and building masonry structures up to damp proof course.

HOW TO INTERPRET INFORMATION FOR SETTING OUT MASONRY STRUCTURES

Setting out

A method of locating the position of building works ready for starting work

Interpret

To understand the meaning of information, eg information from working drawings and specifications

A working bricklayer will be required to **interpret** construction drawings. The drawings are drawn by an architect or an architectural technician. A bricklayer will receive copies of the plans on paper and electronically.

These documents enable the operative to understand the client's requirements and, more importantly, will show just what the client is paying for. The drawings you use on a daily basis will depend on the structure itself. If you are building a detached house, the number of drawings can be determined by how complex the design of the dwelling is and may incorporate up to ten different, individual drawings.

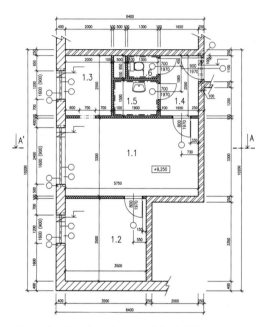

Example of a drawing used by bricklayers

Each drawing will show you a different view of the dwelling and help you understand the trowel work which will be required, eg the brick or blockwork below the DPC level (the substructure) and the brick or blockwork above the DPC level (the superstructure).

Elevations

To view a faced plan of a building, eg front, rear and sides

Cross-section

On a drawing, a view of an internal section of a wall as though it has been cut in half

Isometric projections

To view an object at an angle of 30°

The drawings will show you the different **elevations**, such as front and rear elevations, alongside plan (bird's eye) views and **cross-section** views. They will include information about everything from the position of the site to the position of the walls being constructed. The plans will show the assembly and sections. For further information the architect will also supply **isometric projections**. Being able to read a working drawing takes practice.

When a contract is started, the drawings enable the operative to plan from the very first day.

DRAWINGS USED IN SETTING OUT

We will now look at the different areas on the drawings.

BLOCK PLANS

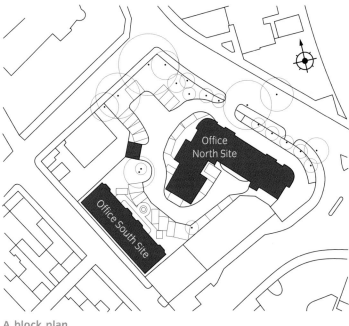

A block plan

The above block plan shows how a bricklayer would read the location of the site, adjoining roads and **boundary** lines. It's common practice to highlight the working area in a different colour to make it clearer.

One advantage of the block plan is that it allows bricklayers and builders to plan their daily parking requirements. In many situations, parking becomes difficult if site access is blocked.

Another advantage of this bird's eye view of the site is the boundaries. The clear dividing line between properties can be determined. Good, clear drawings and photographs can also help when individuals have a problem about the ownership of land and buildings. These drawings can help to resolve disputes.

Boundary

A line marking the end of an area

INDUSTRY TIP

Not all drawing dimensions work to scale. Always check the full scale requirements on site and confirm the measurements with the line manager, architect or client.

FLOOR PLANS

This bird's eye view of the planned construction is often the most informative one for a bricklayer. The general layout of the building, shown floor by floor, is easily definable. A good drawing will always show the dimensions of the rooms and the structure.

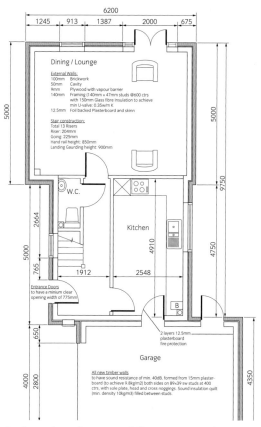

A clear plan of a ground floor construction

Measurements and dimensions are always written in metric form (see Chapter 2). The plan view allows bricklayers to take the sizes of the structure and relate these measurements to the site.

ELEVATIONS

Front elevation

A front elevation plan

This elevation generally shows the:

■ entrance

■ window and door configuration

■ shape of the roof.

This view can be the most informative one for bricklayers and operatives.

Details about access to the front door of a **property** can be found on the block plan.

The elevation may also show substructure brick and blockwork and superstructure brick and blockwork. This example includes the brickwork (BWK) for the chimney construction.

Rear elevation

A rear elevation plan

Like the front elevation, this elevation also generally shows the:

- entrance

- window and door configuration

- shape of the roof.

Details about rear access will be shown with this type of elevation. Information about the garden area and any patio surface will be found on drawings relating to floor plans.

SECTION VIEWS

The **section drawings** are always informative and give bricklayers a view of the inside of the structure being built.

Drawings showing a cross-section use **hatchings** to indicate what type of resource is to be used. An example of a hatching symbol is two diagonal lines close together at an angle of 45° used for brickwork. See Chapter 2, page 48 for more examples of these symbols.

Section drawings

Repeated views of different structures

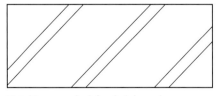

Hatching symbol for brickwork

Hatching

Patterns used on a drawing to identify different materials to meet the standard BS1192

OUR HOUSE

Look at 'Our House' and imagine it as a drawing. What hatching symbols would be used on the plan to show the different materials in the house?

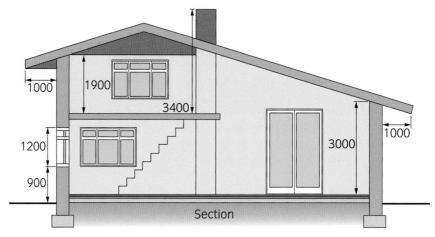

A diagram of a cross-section of a house. Measurements are in mm

Many section drawings continue underground and give bricklayers information about the foundation type and size.

SCALES

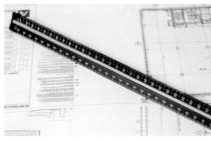

A scale rule on a set of plans

For ease of use and understanding the architect will draw the plans using a scale. By using a scale rule, you can convert the scale to a measurement which will in turn allow you to work out the required measurements to establish the setting out positions for the job in hand.

The common scales for bricklayers are:

- 1:500
- 1:100
- 1:20
- 1:10
- 1:5
- 1:2
- 1:1.

Full-sized drawings are scaled 1:1. They might be used for detailed window or door cills to show close up detail for bricklayers to follow For more information about scales, see Chapter 2, page 47.

PREPARING FOR SETTING OUT

CHECKING TOOLS

It is important to check your tools and equipment for accuracy before you use them. We will look at this in more detail on pages 112–115.

SITE CLEARANCE

When first working on a green or brown field site, important safety aspects need to be considered.

SUBSOIL

The site will, at some point, need to be cleared of all vegetable matter (**top soil**) and subsoil. This is because subsoil is very weak with regard to the loading of a structure. Most subsoil has a depth of about 150mm. Building regulations state that all the subsoil must be removed because it has a low load-bearing capacity. This soil can be reused at a later date when making good the outside areas.

Top soil

The top 150mm of soil containing vegetable matter

SERVICES

When setting out, the first approach to clearing the site can bring to light many problems, which may not be found until the top surface material has been removed.

The site may contain buried pipework or even electrical cables. The services need to be detected and removed or moved to another location by competent persons. This will prevent accidents, and possibly deaths, occurring in the early stages of construction.

The equipment used for detecting the services can be purchased or hired to enable the bricklayer to work with confidence on the foundations of the structure. The photograph on the left shows a typical **detector**. This piece of equipment works by sending out an electronic pulse. When metal is found underground the pulse is bounced back to the detector. The detector can tell how deep the metal is by measuring the time it takes for the pulse to return.

A detector for finding metal cables underground

Detector

Equipment used to locate the services

RECLAIMING MATERIALS

When starting a project, many different types of materials may be found and **reclaimed**. For example, the subsoil cleared from the site may be reused for ground works at the end of the project.

Reclaimed

Re use of materials such as crushed bricks and blocks used for hardcore

Recycled

To reuse waste resources for another purpose, eg to crush used brick and blocks to make hardcore

During construction, bricklayers create waste material such as cut bricks and blocks; this waste can be **recycled**.

On building sites we now have waste management systems in place. These allow all waste products to be put into separate skips so they can be reclaimed and reused at a later date.

PERSONAL PROTECTIVE EQUIPMENT

ACTIVITY

Check the date on your safety helmet. Always replace your safety helmet if it is out of date.

INDUSTRY TIP

Never be afraid to ask your employer about supplying PPE to you if you are missing something or if part of your PPE is broken. It is your employer's responsibility to provide it!

Employers have basic duties concerning the provision and use of PPE at work. To find out what employers – and you – must do to meet the requirements of the Personal Protective Equipment (PPE) at Work Regulations 1992, see Chapter 1, pages 20–23.

While setting out on a building site, the following items of PPE are necessary for your protection while using the setting out tools and equipment.

- Safety boots
- Eye protection
- Safety helmet
- Safety overalls
- Safety gloves
- High visibility vest

A bricklayer wearing PPE

SOURCES OF INFORMATION

All construction projects will have written instructions to follow. Instructions could be given by:

- the architect or client in the form of written specifications

- other contract team members, eg the project manager, contract manager or clerk of the works

- the site agent (who will also be a line manager for the site) who will issue instructions to the bricklayers.

The different forms of instructions include:

- working drawings

- risk assessments

- method statements

- specifications

- bill of quantities

- programmes of work.

All documentation must be followed and checked by your line manager as the work proceeds. To record a problem it's best to talk face to face with your line manager. This procedure will not only solve the problem, but also alert other trades. For example, if you received a delivery of bricks and found a problem you should let your line manager know first and then contact the supplier.

For further information about sources of information, see Chapter 2, pages 49–55.

WRITTEN INFORMATION

RISK ASSESSMENTS

Each operative, or their supervisor, must read the risk assessment, which will have been completed by the site supervisor.

Risk Assessment

Assessment carried out by: _____

Date assessment was carried out: _____

Date of next review: _____

Area/ activity	Hazard	Risk to (list persons)	Current precautions	Action	Action required by	Date for required action	Complete

Example of a risk assessment form

The risk assessment will cover all of the tasks relating to the job. Each task is graded as low, medium or high risk. It's important to remember that for each risk, a control measure will have been identified. This must be acted upon. It is very important that you follow the control measures in a risk assessment and your company's procedures. It is vital that you know what to do and who to see when a problem occurs. You can help to ensure that accidents are prevented. Always contact your line manager or tutor if you have a problem with procedures. For more information about risk assessments, see Chapter 1, page 5.

METHOD STATEMENTS

A method statement contains control measures which the bricklayer must follow when constructing a building. For example, when building a cavity wall a bricklayer must have access to bricks and blocks to build the cavity to the required height. This may mean working from scaffolding (ie at height). Working on scaffolding requires the operative to know about and understand how to use access equipment. Hazards such as loading out of materials need to be controlled to reduce the risk of accidents (eg bricks falling from the scaffolding) to either the builders or members of the public. Consideration also needs to be given to other trades working in the area. For more information about method statements, see Chapter 1, page 6.

HEALTH AND SAFETY REGULATIONS

You may be required to co-operate with the principal contractor or client so far as it is necessary to enable them to comply with their duties in accordance with health and safety regulations. This includes following any directions given to you by the principal contractor or client to enable the work to be carried out in a way that meets health and safety regulations.

SPECIFICATIONS

A specification is provided by the architect and is shown clearly so that builders and bricklayers can easily understand and follow it. Specifications include information about the following:

- resources to be used

- measurements

- colours

- **manufacturer's instructions**

- directions

- scales

- contact details, eg telephone numbers and email addresses

- descriptions of the materials to be used.

Manufacturer's instructions

Guidelines given by the manufacturer on conditions of use

INDUSTRY TIP

Always read the specification on the plans. It will enable you to find the correct recommended materials.

CONSTRUCTION SPECIFICATION

VA-745. PLASTIC PIPE

SCOPE

The work shall consist of furnishing and installing plastic pipe and the necessary fittings specified herein or as shown on the drawings. This specification does not cover subsurface drainage systems.

MATERIALS

Poly Vinyl Chloride (PVC) Pipe	
Plastic Pipe - Schedules 40, 80, 120	ASTM D 1785
Pressure Pipe, 4 inches through 12 inches	AWWA C 900
Pressure Rated Pipe - SDR Series	ASTM D 2241
Plastic Drain, Waste, and Vent Pipe and Fittings	ASTM D 2665
Joints for IPS PVC Pipe Using Solvent Cement	ASTM D 2672
ABS and PVC Composite Sewer Pipe	ASTM D 2680
Type PSM PVC Sewer Pipe and Fittings	ASTM D 3034
Large-Diameter Gravity Sewer Pipe and Fittings	ASTM F 679
Smooth-Wall Underdrain Systems for Highway, Airport, and Similar Drainage	ASTM F 758
Type PS-46 Gravity Flow Sewer Pipe and Fittings	ASTM F 789
Profile Gravity Sewer Pipe and Fittings Based on Controlled Inside Diameter	ASTM F 794
Corrugated Sewer Pipe with a Smooth Interior and Fittings	ASTM F 949
Water Transmission Pipe, Nominal Diameters 14-inch	AWWA C 905

Example of a specification used with a working drawing. This provides detail which a working drawing cannot show.

The bricklayer will refer to the specification, along with other key documents, before, during and on completion of the project to ensure that the criteria have been met. For more information about specifications, see Chapter 2, page 51.

PROGRAMMES OF WORK

Programme of work

A series of events where the order of activities and the amount of time involved has been planned out

Frontage line

The front edge of the building plot

Building line

The front line of the building. Note: this can be on or behind the frontage line

The **programme of work** relating to a contract will have details about the timescales, trades involved and the activities to be carried out. It's very important the programme is followed as closely as possible. If the programme falls behind in any way, eg due to bad weather, the schedule will be affected and the natural follow on of the trades may be delayed. It is vital to communicate with your line manager if a programme delay is forecast. Setting out both the **frontage** and **building lines** (see pages 115–116) will be among the first programmed activities highlighted on the programme of work.

CHOOSING THE CORRECT RESOURCES FOR SETTING OUT

COMMON BRICKLAYING RESOURCES

During the course of building a wall a bricklayer will use many different types of:

Aggregates

The coarse mineral material, such as sharp sand and graded, crushed stone (gravel), used in making mortar and concrete

- materials, including **aggregates** (chippings and sand)
- tools
- equipment.

However, when setting out a bricklayer will have limited materials. The following materials, resources and tools can be used to help set out and mark dimensions:

Profile

1) Timber or metal frame designed to position straight and cornered profiles with straight ranging lines attached

2) Boards fixed horizontally to ground pegs at the ends of a wall before construction commences in order that lines may be stretched across to mark the position of the wall

- aggregates
- lime
- cement
- water
- bricks
- blocks
- timber pegs
- **profiles**

- a ranging line

- **straight edge** (timber or metal)

- tape measure

- nails

- **builder's square**

- optical level

- spirit level

- hand tools.

Using these tools and resources on site will help to identify the setting out lines, ready for the excavator to remove the subsoil and create the foundation trenches.

TAPE MEASURES

A range of tape measures in various sizes is required when setting out a structure. Tape measures vary in length from 3m to 30m.

Check your tape measure for stretching and keep it clean by oiling it.

STRAIGHT EDGES

Always check for alignment by placing a straight edge against a known flat straight surface. Draw a line against it on a flat board then reverse the straight edge. If the line is still next to the straight edge the alignment is accurate. If the line shows a hollow or is round the alignment is inaccurate.

Most straight edges are made from timber or aluminium and range in length from 2m to 5m.

LEVELS

Spirit levels

Spirit levels come in a range of sizes. The size most commonly used by bricklayers is 1.2m. Bricklayers sometimes use 2m spirit levels to help with the construction of blockwork.

Most levels are not **self-adjusting**. The vials need to be replaced or reset.

Optical levels

Modern day **optical** levels are quick and easy to use. They are not costly to purchase. The level is accurate up to 30m with a variation of +/-5mm. Bricklayers use optical levels when the length of construction exceeds the straight edge. Never use a damaged optical level.

Straight edge

An accurately proportioned implement with parallel edges made of timber or aluminium and up to 3m in length

Builder's square

A builder's square set at an angle of 90° will form a right-angled quoin

A short tape measure

An open frame long tape measure

Straight edge

Spirit level

Self-adjusting

Automatic operation built into a levelling instrument

Optical level

Optical

A levelling tool using eyesight

Water level

Calibrate

To ensure no air is trapped in a water level

Perp joints

Perp is short for 'perpendicular'. Small vertical joints which join two bricks together. They are at right angles to the bed

Line and pins

Ranging line

A line stretched between profiles to mark the position of a wall

Water levels

Always **calibrate** your water level prior to use. Check the hose for air bubbles.

A water level is very handy for transferring levels around corners and works up to a range of 10m.

LINE AND PINS

The traditional line and pins method uses the **perp joint** to hold the line taught.

PROFILES

Bricklayers use a range of profiles for all kinds of activities from setting out a structure to building level straight walls. The use of timber profiles when setting out is very important for the alignment of the walls in relation to the plot and foundations.

There are two types of profiles:

- straight profiles
- corner profiles.

Most bricklayers find corner profiles easier to use as they have level lines which can be used to form building lines in two directions.

All profiles must be positioned at least 5m away from the setting out marks to allow for the movement of plant and people. Protecting the profiles during the build will allow the **ranging lines** to be taken off and on as required.

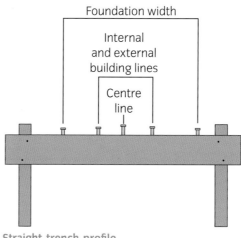

Straight trench profile

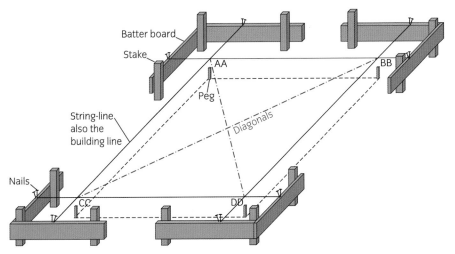

Using four corner profiles to set out

INDUSTRY TIP

Using a corner profile will save on timber because not as many pegs will be required.

You will need good quality ranging lines to create straight profiles

CALCULATING RESOURCES

The quantity of resources required for the setting out process will always be determined by the size of the project. All construction companies have surveying and **levelling** equipment. The quantity of timber or metal required for the profiles is based on the type and size of the house or building.

Levelling

To make sure that two points are at the same height

ASSISTING WITH SETTING OUT

BUILDING AND FRONTAGE LINES

These lines are very important when setting out, and are shown on the drawings. You need to know what the lines represent and who establishes them.

BUILDING LINES

The building line is shown on the drawings and represents the front line of the structure to be built, eg the front wall of a house. This line is established by the architect and the client.

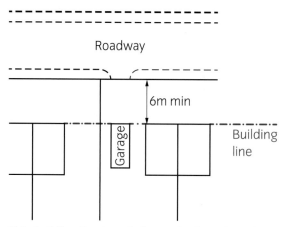

This building line in red shows the front line of the properties

FRONTAGE LINES

The frontage line is established by the architect and the client and shown on the plans. It represents the front edge of the building plot. No construction can be built over the frontage line, ie between the line and the pavement.

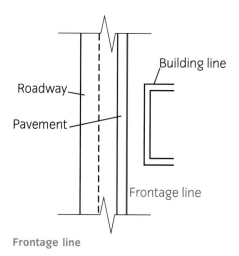

Frontage line

SETTING OUT RIGHT ANGLES

Regular-shaped

To give a square, or rectangular shape to a building or masonry structure

When setting out a **regular-shaped** structure the positioning and accuracy of the measurements is critical. The bricklayer has a tolerance to work to, but if the setting out for square is poorly undertaken this can have a knock-on effect for other trades and the programme of work will be delayed.

HOW TO SET OUT A RIGHT ANGLE

On site, bricklayers use a range of methods and tools to set out a right angle. The most common method is the 3:4:5 ratio. This is a calculation formula used to set out a right angle at 90°. The bricklayer can use metres and the ratios, eg 3m:4m:5m, will form a right angle when setting out.

For example, to set out a right angle using a tape and spirit level use this process:

1 Establish a base line.

2 Measure 400mm along the base line. Call your starting point 'A', and end point B.

3 From 'A', measure 300mm up. This is point C.

4 Join points B and C. This line will be 500mm long.

5 You have formed a right angle at point A.

Calculating the length of the hypotenuse (the longest size of a right angle triangle) is critical in determining the length of the diagonals of a structure.

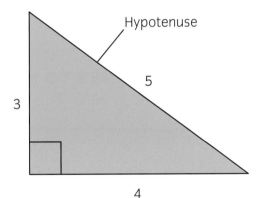

The hypotenuse on a right angle triangle

USING DATUM POINTS

The datum point is a fixed level from which all levels across a building site are taken. For more information on datum points, see Chapter 2, page 47.

INDUSTRY TIP

A timber peg surrounded with concrete or a concrete plinth set at the correct height can be used as a datum point.

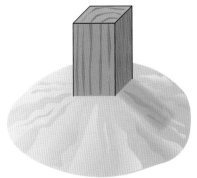

A site datum protected by concrete

Chimney stack

The portion of the chimney containing the tops of the flues which passes through and projects above the roof

Gauge

The vertical setting out of brick courses

On most building sites the datum point will be a fixed peg (a metal rod surrounded by concrete) which is usually positioned near the front entrance and site office for protection. All levels, from the depth of the foundation excavation to the height of the **chimney stack**, can be determined from the site datum point.

Datum heights are very important to bricklayers. The datum heights for brick and blockwork can be marked on the sides of windows and doors to help keep the **gauge** of the materials laid. Two types of datum points are Ordnance bench marks (OBMs) and Temporary bench marks (TBMs), see Chapter 2, page 47 for more information.

see Chapter 2, page 47 for more information.

ACTIVITY

Can you find an OBM? Look near a church or a railway bridge (or any old, longstanding building not likely to have been disturbed) and see if you can find one.

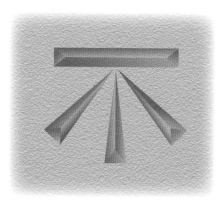

Ordnance bench mark

TRANSFERRING WALL LINES TO FOUNDATION CONCRETE

After fixing the profiles and the ranging lines, the bricklayer must check the setting out against the working drawings, making sure the **alignment** of the building lines is correct.

Alignment

To place something in line

ACTIVITY

The datum height is 1.250m. The finished floor level (FFL) is 150mm below datum. What is the finished floor height?

Answer: 1.1m

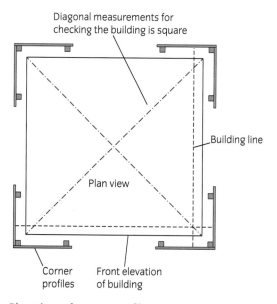

Diagonal measurements for checking the building is square

Building line

Plan view

Corner profiles

Front elevation of building

Plan view of corner profiles

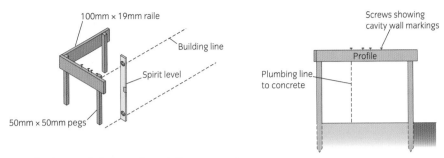

Transferring wall lines to foundation concrete

The drawing above shows the ranging lines, which must be square to one another. The position of the lines can now be transferred to the concrete foundation using a spirit level. The bricklayer will mark the ranging lines at intervals using a thin bed of mortar and a trowel. These marks are then lengthened using a straight edge to give the bricklayer a continuous trowel mark to follow.

SETTING OUT BRICK AND BLOCKWORK

Bricklayers need the materials to be at arm's length. This helps with the production targets and speed of lying. The bricks and blocks need to be 600mm from the face line of the wall being built.

Brick stacks set out

Preparation of the materials on site and in the workshop must always be carried out with health and safety in mind. Materials should not be stacked too high. Where possible, **pallets** should be used and stacked to a maximum height of two pallets. General tidiness when working with trowel trade materials will lend itself to a better overall finish to the walls.

Pallets

A storage base used to carry and store materials

BUILDING STRAIGHT AND CORNERED WALLING

While working as a bricklayer, the correct procedure for the construction of a wall must be followed. The bricklayer will set out the structure to ensure the building works will bond. The **quoin** is built and the infill brickwork is completed using corner blocks or line and pins.

Quoin

The vertical external angles (corners) in walling

An operative building a block wall with stacks of blocks behind him

Straight walling

Cornered walling

JOINTING

Jointing brickwork must be completed while the construction is in progress. The bricklayer can form a range of joint finishes. The most common form is the half-round (bucket handle) joint. At Level 1 the bricklayer will use the half-round, flush and **weather struck** joint finishes.

Jointing

To make a finish to the mortar faces as work proceeds

Weather struck

An angled joint, which means one side of the joint is pressed further into the joint than the other

An operative jointing a solid wall

THE CITY & GUILDS TEXTBOOK

The jointing procedure should always be adhered to. The bricklayer must:

- ensure the bricks are laid with full and complete joints

- work with good timing

- complete the perp joints

- joint from the ends of the wall into the middle.

If the **bed** and perp joints are not full and complete, the bricklayer must infill the joints with a pointing trowel prior to using the **jointer**.

Bed joint

Continuous, horizontal mortar joint supporting the bricks

Jointer

A tool used for making a jointed finish

INDUSTRY TIP

Perp joints are finished first when applying weather struck.

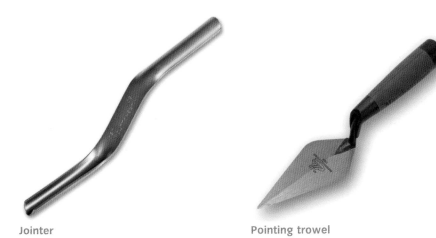

Jointer   Pointing trowel

Case Study: Matthew and Amy

Matthew and Amy are to build their own house. Setting out and undertaking as much of the work as possible themselves is a great way of saving time and money.

Matthew has worked in the construction industry for five years as a bricklayer and has experience of setting out and constructing both brick and blockwork. Using tools and equipment such as working drawings, scale rules and tape measures is part of the educational experience of studying towards most vocational trades. Matthew has the experience and Amy can provide an extra pair of hands and contribute to the setting out of their house.

Matthew knows that conducting a risk assessment before setting out is very important. Matthew and Amy will check the location and description of all the services such as gas, water, electricity and drainage. No excavation or driving of pegs will be undertaken until the site investigation has taken place.

Matthew also knows the importance of taking scaled measurements from an original drawing and not from a copy. The drawing will show the required lengths of walling and Matthew, with the help of Amy, can transfer these measurements to the ground using datum points and setting out pegs.

Both Matthew and Amy know the frontage and building lines are the two setting out lines and positions that must be checked for accuracy and position. Amy has double checked these measurements with both the architect and the local authority. Once the setting out pegs have been positioned, the checks for square can be undertaken again. Amy can assist with the tapes and marking peg positions. Now Matthew and Amy will be able to establish the profiles and ranging lines to set out the complete shape of their new house.

Work through the following questions to check your learning.

1 Which **one** of the following shows a new house in relation to its surroundings?

   a   Section plan

   b   Block plan

   c   Street plan

   d   Building plan

2 What is the hypotenuse?

   a   Longest side of a right angle triangle

   b   Shortest side of a right angle triangle

   c   A 90° angle

   d   A 45° angle

3 Which of these is not a type of joint?

   a   Half-round

   b   Flush

   c   Weather struck

   d   Mouse ears

4 What is the starting position for transferring a level?

   a   Fixed point

   b   Concrete point

   c   Datum point

   d   Gauged point

5 What is the most common form of joint finish?

   a   Weather struck

   b   Weather struck and cut

   c   Recess

   d   Half-round

6 What does the abbreviation BWK stand for?

   a   Brickwork

   b   Blockwork

   c   Building

   d   Boardwalk

7 On a working drawing, what is 1:1 equal to?

   a   Full size

   b   Half size

   c   Quarter size

   d   Twice the size

8 When setting out a right angle, what ratio do bricklayers use?

   a   3:6:9

   b   3:4:5

   c   1:4:8

   d   6:7:9

9 Which **one** of these would a front elevation drawing not show you?

   a   Entrance

   b   Shape of the roof

   c   Window and door configuration

   d   Furniture

10 Which of these is not a type of measuring tool?

   a   Straight edge

   b   Aggregates

   c   Line and pins

   d   Tape measure

11 What is this a picture of?

   a   Water level

   b   Laying trowel

   c   Pointing trowel

   d   Rasp

12 Which of the following can be used to check a corner for square?

a Builder's square

b Carpentry square

c Plumber's square

d Electrical square

13 Which document do operatives have a responsibility to read?

a Risk assessment

b Newspaper

c Health and safety manual

d Instructions

14 What is this a picture of?

a Rod

b Pole

c Stick

d Jointer

15 What is this a picture of?

a Clothes line

b Builder's line

c String

d Wire

16 When applying a weather struck finish, which joint is pointed first?

a End of the bed joint

b Middle of the bed joint

c Perp joint

d Bottom bed joint

17 Where will the technical details on a working drawing be located?

a Specification

b Bill of quantities

c Contract

d Email

18 What is the maximum length that water levels work to?

a 2m

b 4m

c 6m

d 10m

19 What item of equipment is best when transferring a long level?

a Boat level

b Optical level

c Pocket level

d Line level

20 To maintain accuracy, what should a builder's square be?

a As small as possible

b As angled as possible

c As large as possible

d As light as possible

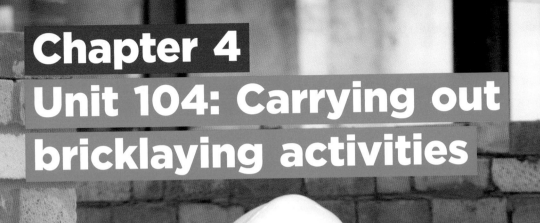

Chapter 4
Unit 104: Carrying out bricklaying activities

This chapter discusses the skills and knowledge required to carry out basic bricklaying tasks. Mastering the task of assembling bricks and mortar to produce a wall or other structure requires patience and practice. Persevere in developing your skills and knowledge and you will have an ability that will provide you with great job satisfaction as well as a good living. Become an expert in your trade and you will gain the respect of those who value a good job.

By reading this chapter you will know how to:

1 Prepare for bricklaying activities in accordance with work specifications.

2 Build brick walling, returns and junctions in half-brick Stretcher bond.

3 Use bricks to build walling.

PREPARE RESOURCES FOR BUILDING BRICK WALLING

With most activities in life, the key to success is preparation. Laying bricks is no different: success depends on good preparation. That's why becoming a good bricklayer depends on more than learning just the trade skills. You also need to develop skills in planning and organising as well as learning to work efficiently with others.

Most importantly, good preparation means getting the right mind-set about health and safety. There are materials used in construction that must be treated with care. Make it a habit to consult the relevant Control of Substances Hazardous to Health (COSHH) statements. This is a protection to you and those around you.

Building sites and construction workshops can be dangerous places with many potential hazards. Chapter 1 provides lots of important detail about the many laws and regulations.

When preparing for your brickwork tasks in the workshop or the workplace, the first step is to get familiar with exactly what it is that you are building. To ensure you know all the relevant details of the job, you will need to refer to a working drawing and a specification. (For more on drawings including scale, hatchings and symbols, refer back to pages 47–48.)

The drawing and specification will tell you what types of materials are to be used and may tell you something about the methods of work to be used. They will also help you to select the right tools and equipment for the task in hand.

TOOLS

Let's look at the range of tools needed for basic bricklaying. You will recognise some of these from Chapter 3. We can split the tools into three main groups. Tools for:

- *Laying and finishing.* To build any wall you will need a trowel to lay the bricks, a pointing trowel and a jointer to provide a finish to the joints.

Trowel

Pointing trowel

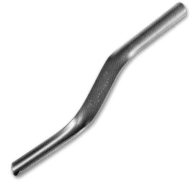

Jointer

THE CITY & GUILDS TEXTBOOK

■ *Checking*. A spirit level is needed to make sure the work is level and plumb, a set of line and pins to align the bricks accurately and a tape measure to set out and check dimensions.

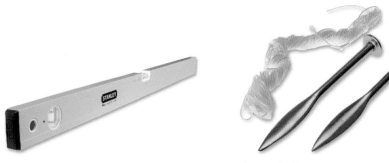

Spirit level | Line and pins | Tape measure

■ *Cutting*. To cut the bricks you will need a club (or lump) hammer and a brick bolster. There are additional tools to cut bricks for different purposes such as a brick hammer and a **scutch hammer** (sometimes called a comb hammer).

Scutch hammer

A bricklayer's hammer with interchangeable finishing heads for trimming and tidying bricks and blocks

Club hammer

Brick bolster

Brick hammer

Scutch hammer

The correct way to use all of these tools will be discussed later.

Architects are responsible for choosing the right brick for a structure

Efflorescence

A white deposit which may form on the surface of new bricks if the latter contain a high proportion of mineral salts

MATERIALS

BRICKS

Bricks are manufactured in a vast range of colours and textures. They also vary in hardness or compressive strength and resistance to moisture penetration according to the materials used in manufacture. Choosing the right brick for a particular location or type of structure is therefore very important. The architect and his or her design team are responsible for specifying the right brick.

It's good to develop the habit of checking that the bricks and other materials you intend to use are actually the ones specified. If you find that the materials are the wrong type, size or colour, never just 'carry on regardless'. Always check the specification with your supervisor or line manager and talk to them about any problems.

It's also good to develop the habit of thinking ahead about protecting the bricks and other materials. Having polythene sheeting or other protection to hand is good practice at the preparation stage. The materials should be protected from adverse weather at all times. Bricks are difficult to lay accurately and neatly when wet.

Bricks protected by polythene sheeting

Laying wet bricks can contribute to a problem known as **efflorescence**, which disfigures the appearance of brickwork by leaving a white powder deposited on the surface of the wall. Although this can be removed by brushing with a stiff brush, it's better to avoid the problem by maintaining good practice in the first place.

Efflorescence

Once work is completed, it will still need to be protected from adverse weather and other construction operations.

Everyone in the workplace must contribute to safety and efficiency by:

- taking care to minimise damage to work

- keeping the work area clean and tidy

- disposing of waste properly.

Waste is often **segregated** to support recycling and contribute to sustainability.

Segregated

Separated into groups or categories (eg glass, metal, wood)

Segregated waste skips on a site for paper and cardboard and wood

Since bricks can be a heavy building material, it is very important to give careful consideration to health and safety matters when moving them. Always use proper handling techniques and wear suitable PPE. A basic set of PPE items for a bricklayer handling materials would include: safety boots, safety glasses or goggles and gloves. Chapter 1, pages 20–23, covers these points in more detail but, when preparing and placing materials prior to building brickwork, remember that *bricks are heavy and often sharp*.

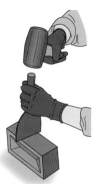

A club hammer and brick bolster are used to cut bricks

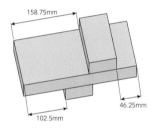

Brick gauge

Cutting bricks

Sharp edges are also produced when we need to cut bricks. We may need to cut bricks for a number of reasons which we will discuss later. For now, let's look at the tools needed and the methods we should use to cut bricks by hand (cutting by machine is often preferred on site but requires extensive training in safe practices).

Cutting bricks is an operation that can only be mastered with experience, so be prepared to have disappointments at first! The main cutting tools have been listed previously. The primary tools are a club (or lump) hammer and a brick bolster. Another useful tool not mentioned above, which aids in producing accurate and consistent cuts, is a brick gauge. This is made from timber and can be easily made on site. The different parts of the cutting gauge allow you to easily and accurately mark the measurements for a half-bat, three-quarter bat and a Queen Closer.

Whether we use a brick gauge or a tape measure and pencil to mark the brick, always aim for accuracy. This will make producing a quality piece of brickwork a much easier task.

Many bricks have good compressive strength but are brittle and shatter easily. To improve the chances of success in cutting, therefore, it's good practice to place the brick to be cut on a small mound of sand which will act as a cushion. Alternatives such as sacking or old carpet could also be used. Make sure the *whole surface area* of whichever face is on the cushion is supported. Let's look at the process.

STEP 1 Make sure you are using the right PPE (safety glasses or goggles etc) and workers nearby are aware that you are cutting bricks.

STEP 2 Mark the position of the cut on the face, the opposite side and the bed of the brick with a pencil.

STEP 3 Place the brick with the face uppermost Placing the blade of the bolster slightly on the *waste* side of the pencil mark, strike it lightly but firmly with the club hammer.

STEP 4 Now do the same on the opposite side of the brick.

STEP 5 Turn the brick so that the face is uppermost again and strike the last blow. If the strength of the blow is adjusted correctly, this should complete the operation (remember – experience counts).

STEP 6 If the brick doesn't break as desired, repeat from Step 3 until a clean break is achieved.

The aim is to produce clean sharp edges especially on the face side of the cut brick. This will ensure a good appearance in the finished wall. If there are rough projections or edges, then a scutch hammer can be used to trim the cut brick and to make precise adjustments. The other cutting tool mentioned in our previous list is a brick hammer. This can also be used for trimming bricks but it is less precise and is usually used to quickly produce rougher cuts where appearance is not so important.

High standards in selecting, moving, cutting or laying bricks depends on skill, care and attention and the use of the correct tools and techniques. This is no less true with the other important material used by the bricklayer: mortar.

MORTAR

Whilst it is usually the case that mortar is mixed and brought to the bricklayer by semi-skilled operatives, it is the bricklayer's responsibility to make sure that the material is fit for purpose and is used in accordance with the specification.

Mortar is the material we use to **bed** and joint the bricks together. It is mainly composed of **well graded** sand (either 'pit sand' or 'sea-dredged sand') and Ordinary Portland Cement (often referred to as OPC) mixed to a specified ratio. There are other types of cement which you will learn about later in your studies. Mixing these two component materials together with water will produce a mix that is difficult to use, so a plasticiser is added to improve workability. This usually comes in the form of a chemical additive that traps tiny bubbles of air in the mix, which allows the grains of sand to move over each other more freely.

Traditionally, hydrated lime in powder form was added as a plasticiser. As there are some safety hazards to consider in using

INDUSTRY TIP

Since different types of brick can vary in hardness, it's sometimes better to make the final cutting stroke on the bed of the brick. With experience you will learn the best approach.

Bed

Mortar upon which the brick is laid or bedded

Well graded

Having large, medium and small grains

ACTIVITY

What items of PPE do you think you might need to use when cutting bricks? Make a list, starting with 'Safety glasses or goggles'.

Plasticiser

Dry silo mixer

A major piece of equipment that contains all the dry materials to produce mortar mixed on demand

Ready mix arriving on a site

lime and it is not used so often since the introduction of safer, easier to use chemical additives.

On site, mortar can be mixed as required in a drum mixer. A more modern approach is to use a **dry silo mixer.** Both these methods minimise waste since they produce mortar as it is needed. The silo mixer has the advantage of producing mortar of dependable quality and consistency which is particularly important if coloured mortar is specified. An alternative is to have mortar delivered to site in a ready-mixed form. This method of production requires a chemical additive to slow down the setting time so that the material remains workable throughout a working day.

Dry silo mixer

Drum mixer

An operative mixing by hand

There will still be occasions when there will be a need to mix mortar by hand for smaller jobs. For example, a small garden wall may be difficult to access with machinery such as a mixer, so mixing by hand will be the only option. Whatever method is used to mix mortar, always keep in mind the hazards associated with the materials used. These are covered in more detail in Chapter 1, but when preparing and placing mixing materials prior to building brickwork, remember that *cement and lime powders can irritate your skin and* aggregates *are heavy to move especially when wet.*

ACTIVITY

Research the health effects of irritation from cement and lime dust. Find out what diseases can be caused.

QUANTITIES

This section on preparation for bricklaying tasks would not be complete without considering the subject of quantities. Many construction workers shy away from carrying out calculations of quantities, perhaps thinking that it's too complex for them to deal with. Whether we work in the workshop or out on site, being able to calculate the amount of materials for the job is very important.

Think about it: if we can't calculate the correct amount of materials for a task, we might run out of materials before we finish it. On site, losing time means losing money. At the end of a working week, we will need to know how much money we have earned. If we can't calculate the quantity of work completed, we won't know how much we should be paid. To see how simple it can be to work things out, look at the examples below. The examples focus on two aspects of calculating quantities: *area* and *linear* measurements.

When you are calculating quantities, the *area* of a wall is the size of its surface, so when you look at the face of a brick wall you are looking at the *area* you need to calculate. For more general information on area, refer to Chapter 2, page 62.

Although measurements on a working drawing are normally stated in millimetres, we calculate the surface area in square metres. Each square metre contains 60 bricks so by multiplying the number of square metres by 60, we can work out the number of bricks we need for a wall. Always add an amount to cover wastage (eg 5%).

If our wall dimensions are in whole metres the job is very easy – we can just count up the square metre 'boxes'.

A quantity surveyor at work

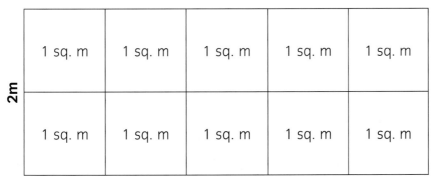

This example has an area of 10m².

However, it's rarely the case that we build walls like this, so we need to remember the simple formula to work out areas for walls that are not whole metres from Chapter 2: *Area = length multiplied by height.* Using a calculator makes it very easy to work things out.

Example 1

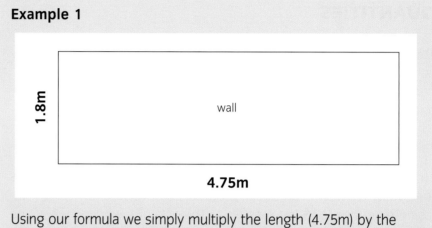

Using our formula we simply multiply the length (4.75m) by the height (1.8m) to produce our area in m² (or square metres). So our calculation to work out the area of our wall would look like this:

$$4.75 \times 1.8 = 8.55m^2$$

The total wall area is **8.55m²**.

Now just multiply 8.55 by the number of bricks to a square metre (60) and we've got the number of bricks for our wall. Don't forget to add an amount for wastage. Simple!

So what about *linear* measurements? As the name suggests, linear measurements involve working with dimension along a line. Sometimes an overall dimension is split up into smaller parts.

ACTIVITY

Try working with someone else to practise this. Take turns in thinking up wall dimensions that are not whole metres and calculate the areas in square metres. Keep the dimensions for length and height sensible – up to a maximum of 10m long and 2m high. Check each other's work and discuss any errors that you make.

Example 2

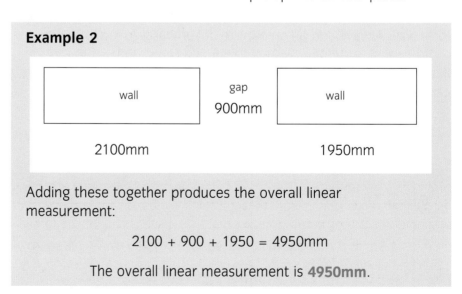

Adding these together produces the overall linear measurement:

$$2100 + 900 + 1950 = 4950mm$$

The overall linear measurement is **4950mm**.

Notice these dimensions are written as millimetres. This is usual practice in construction working drawings. To convert millimetres to metres we simply move the decimal point three places to the left.

Example 3

With 4950mm the decimal point is here: 4950.

Move it three places to the left and it ends up here: 4.950, which now reads as 4 metres and 950 millimetres.

Calculating quantities for mortar is more difficult, but there are many free calculating tools online that are specifically designed for the purpose and are easy to use.

Preparation of resources is all about thinking ahead and planning carefully. If you make good preparation a habit, your work will be more enjoyable and productive and you will be able to build brickwork to high standards that will be valued by employers and customers throughout your career.

SET OUT TO BUILD BRICK WALLING TO GIVEN INSTRUCTIONS

After preparing our tools, checking our materials, and having calculated our quantities, we can arrange our work area and set up our work task. Once again careful preparation is important to success. The main consideration from the outset is to set up our work area safely. The safety and welfare of construction personnel and members of the public who may be affected by construction operations is protected by many laws and regulations. They are detailed in Chapter 1. Review them frequently.

Remember that, as an individual in the workshop or on site, you are responsible for your own health, safety and welfare and for that of the people including those around you. There are serious consequences for being **negligent**.

Moving heavy materials like bricks is best done by mechanical means if possible. On site, it's likely that a forklift will be the main piece of machinery used for moving heavy materials. The driver of the forklift is trained to work in a safe manner. Cooperate with his or her instructions when setting up the work area. If bricks *have* to be moved by hand, use **kinetic lifting** techniques, see pages 18–19 of Chapter 1.

Forklift

Negligent

Being careless or neglectful

Kinetic lifting

A method of lifting that ensures that the risk of injury is reduced

INDUSTRY TIP

Get to know the forklift driver. Since it's likely he/she will be moving most of your heavy materials for you, it's a good idea to build a positive relationship.

Bricks are usually delivered to site in packs of several hundreds. The number in each pack will vary depending on the weight of the brick – heavier bricks will have fewer in the pack. The packs are 'banded' together using steel or heavy-duty nylon bands to prevent the bricks spilling out. Removing these bands needs to be done with care. Use a proper cutting tool such as metal snips, and wear the correct PPE. Gloves, safety goggles and safety boots should be worn whilst opening packs of bricks. *Never leave the bands lying around* – they will be a dangerous trip hazard.

Metal snips should be used for removing bands on stacks of bricks

Banded pallets of bricks

ACTIVITY

Write a simple risk assessment detailing the potential hazards associated with moving and handling bricks on site. Include moving materials by machine and by hand. You will need to list the risks, who could be affected and what you can do to minimise the risks you have identified.

Loose brick bands can be a trip hazard

Once the materials are near the work area, they will need to be arranged so that the bricklayer can work efficiently. It's often the case that bricklayers work in teams of two bricklayers and a general operative (often referred to as a '2 and 1 gang'). During the early stages of setting up the job, it's a good idea if the loading out is shared by the whole team, in order to get the actual bricklaying started as soon as possible. The bricks should be arranged in neat stacks.

Some tradespersons set out stacks with 12 bricks to each layer in the stack. Whatever pattern is preferred, the stacks should be as stable as possible, so it may be necessary to spend some time levelling the area when stacking at ground level. Stacking out on scaffolding is simpler since the deck of the scaffold is level and even. However, preparing the work area and the actual process of building requires greater care and awareness when working at height. There may be personnel working in the area below the scaffold who could be severely injured if materials were to fall on them from above. Wherever the stacking takes place, at ground level or on scaffold, never stack too high!

An important point to keep in mind when stacking out is to make sure that the bricks are mixed or **blended**. This is because the colour of bricks can vary from batch to batch, due to variations in the manufacturing conditions and the materials used. Mixing bricks by selecting them from a minimum of three packs whilst loading out will help to avoid bands of colour showing in the completed work.

An operative levelling ground prior to stacking bricks

Blended

Having gone through a process that disperses variations in colour and size of bricks to avoid unwanted patterns emerging

ACTIVITY

When you travel around, see if you can spot some examples of **banding** in brickwork in your area. If you have one, use your mobile phone to take a photograph and show your tutor and fellow students.

Banding

Whole sections of brickwork that differ in colour and stand out from the main body of work

Operatives working with stacks of bricks on a level scaffold

So that the bricklayer can work efficiently, the stacks of bricks should be positioned about 600mm from the face line of the wall to be built.

Example of banding in a brick wall

Spot board

A board made of durable material roughly 600mm x 600mm, on which mortar is placed

This allows enough space to work and move without the bricklayer having to stretch too far to pick up a brick. Think about it – if a bricklayer has to take two steps to reach a stack of bricks for every brick laid, and he or she lays 500 bricks in a day, how much time and energy has been wasted? A lot!

The same principle applies to positioning the mortar. The mortar mix is placed on a **spot board**, which is raised up from ground level by supporting it on blocks. Along the line of the wall there should be alternate stacks of bricks and spot boards to allow continuous laying along the full length of the wall with the same pattern of materials continuing around corners.

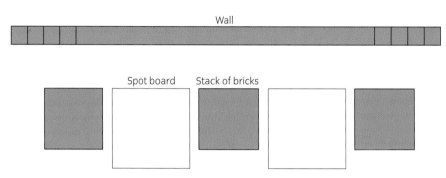

Spot boards with mortar next to a wall of five courses

Once the materials are safely moved to the work area and positioned for efficient working, we can begin the job of setting out the wall ready for building.

SETTING OUT

Bricks are manufactured to dimensions and tolerances decided by official institutes. In the UK, the British Standards Institute (see Chapter 2, page 47) has in the past been the agency that produced official standards and gave numbers to components so that the details about them could be easily checked. Now the European Union has more control and the numbers have changed. For example, clay bricks used to have the number BS 3921. This has now changed to BS EN 771–1.

Look at the illustration of a brick. It shows the names of the various parts of a brick and its dimensions. *In time you should know these off by heart.*

Due to variations in the quality of materials and the manufacturing processes, bricks can vary slightly in overall size. By varying the size of the mortar joint between bricks, we can accommodate these differences, but the size of the joint should not vary by more than 3mm. This means that the maximum joint size should be 13mm and

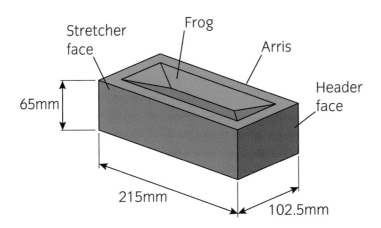

Dimensions and parts of a brick

Stretcher Face

The long face of a brick when laid

Frog

The indentation of a brick

Arris

Any straight sharp edge of a brick formed by the junction of two faces

Header Face

The end face of a brick

the minimum joint size should be 7mm. You will learn more about these and BS testing at Level 2.

It's good practice to set out a wall **dry** before laying the bricks in mortar, especially if the wall has to be built to specific linear dimensions. (Note: Setting out wall dimensions is different to setting out a building. Setting out a complete building is done before excavation of the foundation trenches can take place.) Setting out the first course dry means we can check whether the joint sizes will be suitable and either tighten or open up the **perp joints** so that the wall will fit within the specified dimensions. This is often referred to as setting out the bond.

Dry

Spacing bricks without mortar to sort out potential problems with the bond

Perp joints

Small vertical joints which join two bricks together

Setting out dry: notice there is no mortar between the bricks

TYPES OF BOND

HALF-BOND

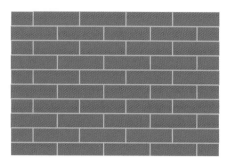

Stretcher bond

The most common bond is Stretcher bond. The name refers to the long face of the brick, which is called the 'stretcher' face, see the illustration on the previous page. In Stretcher bond the bricks are arranged with an overlap the width of a brick (102.5mm). This means that the perp joints are exactly halfway along the face of the stretchers in the course below, so Stretcher bond is often called half-bond. Since the width of the wall is almost the same as half a brick, we refer to Stretcher bond as half-brick walling.

A good building design will be arranged so that the overall dimensions work to full brick sizes. But this is not always possible and, if varying the joint sizes doesn't make things fit, the bricklayer will have to use other methods. One method is to 'reverse' the bond. This means that rather than the wall having matching headers (or stretchers) at either end, the bonding arrangement is reversed so that there will be a header at one end and a stretcher at the other end.

Reverse bond

If this doesn't produce a wall with uniform joints within the overall measurements, then the only choice is to cut the bricks to suitable dimensions. Placing cut bricks within a course of brickwork is called broken bond. The smallest cut allowed is known as a half-bat and measures 102.5mm, the same as the header face of a full brick.

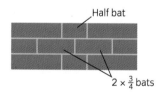

Broken bond

Cut bricks in broken bond should be placed as near to the centre of the wall as possible. If there are doors or windows in the wall, the broken bond can be placed underneath one of them. When a half-bat is built into a course of brickwork, the course above and below it will contain two three-quarter cuts (or bats) to maintain the bond.

If the decision is to cut the bricks to establish proper bonding, then we need to use the methods and tools already discussed in the previous section.

Since it is important to maintain accuracy in building our wall, we need to ensure that the first course that we lay is level and accurately aligned, as required by the working drawing. The next section will discuss in detail the methods and sequence we use to achieve this.

QUARTER BOND

Whilst Stretcher bond can be termed half-bond, there are other bonds which can be termed Quarter bond. The most common of these are Flemish bond and English bond. These are used where a thicker wall is needed for greater strength. Using these bonds results in a wall that has a width equal to the length of the stretcher face of a brick (215mm) and are therefore referred to as 'one-brick' walling.

Flemish bond

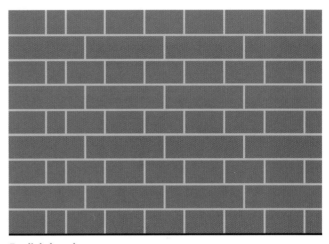

English bond

BONDING ARRANGEMENTS

The bonding arrangement in Stretcher bond is quite straightforward, but a bricklayer needs to understand how all of these different kinds of bond are laid out, in order to set out walls effectively. An old saying states 'Bricklayer can't bond – Bricklayer can't build', so we need to examine bonding in more detail. We'll concentrate on one-brick walling or Quarter bond for a moment.

Take note of the width of a brick: 102.5mm. Why bother with 0.5 (half) of a millimetre? It's important because bricks are designed to be assembled together in **modular** patterns.

In a modular arrangement, two header faces with a 10mm joint between them will add up exactly to the length of the stretcher face of a brick (102.5 + 10 + 102.5 = 215m). This is useful when we want to create the first course of the end of a wall in one-brick walling.

However, when we want to set out a corner, we will find it difficult to achieve the correct bonding arrangement without adding a specially cut component to maintain Quarter bond. This component is called a

End of an English bond wall with two headers above a stretcher

Modular

Designed with standardised units or dimensions for easy assembly

Queen Closer

A brick split along its length to produce a cut of 46mm

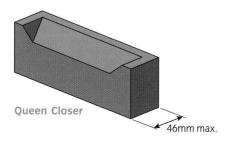

Queen Closer

46mm max.

Queen Closer. Take some time to study the illustrations of English bond and Flemish bond (covered later in this chapter) and note where the Queen Closer is placed in each course.

Flemish bonding layout

English bonding layout

We can build walls with a width greater than the length of one brick using these bonds in modified bonding arrangements. You will learn about these as you progress to higher levels of study. The wider the wall, the greater the strength and the higher it can be built within set limits.

HEIGHT OF WORK

Of course, limits must be applied to the height of any brick wall during the construction process since the mortar must be given time to set to its working strength. Masonry is relatively fragile until the mortar is completely set and the wall is integrated into a building or complete structure. A wall built from heavy components, like bricks laid in a soft material like mortar, can be vulnerable to strong winds blowing into the face. For this reason care must be exercised by the bricklayer not to build too high in one working day.

The optimum height to which a wall can be built in one work period will be determined by the type of brick, the consistency of the mortar, and the weather conditions, both at the time of building and expected in the near future. As a rule of thumb, be cautious about building unsupported brickwork higher than 12 courses at one time (especially for half-brick walling). Whilst it's possible to build higher than this, the specification for a particular job may actually direct the bricklayer to build to fewer than 12 courses at one time, sometimes as few as six courses. If in doubt, ask your supervisor or line manager.

Carefully setting out the work area and the brickwork task prior to actually commencing laying bricks achieves a number of things:

- supports safe practice both in the workshop and on site

- increases efficiency and productivity

- highlights potential problems and difficulties before they become expensive to rectify

- assists in producing good-quality work.

BUILD STRAIGHT BRICK WALLING AND RETURN CORNERS IN HALF-BRICK STRETCHER BOND TO THE GIVEN INSTRUCTIONS

We now come to the actual laying of bricks to produce a wall or structure that conforms to a working drawing and a specification. Having taken care in preparation, we need to extend this standard of care into our bricklaying activity. Skilled bricklayers with years of experience behind them are a pleasure to watch as they carefully produce a high-quality piece of work.

Experience is obviously not something that can be gained overnight, so be patient. Practice, perseverance and developing the habit of scrutinising your own work is the only way to become more proficient and skilled. The techniques required to manage and manipulate the materials used in bricklaying will be repeated over and over throughout your career. Let's examine them.

A skilled bricklayer at work

ROLLING MORTAR

Blade

The 'working' part of the trowel that allows manipulation of the mortar

Rolling mortar on the spot board is the traditional way of preparing the material to lay a bed joint. A portion of mortar is cut from the heap on the board and, with the **blade** of the trowel held vertically, a roll is formed by a back-and-forth horizontal movement across the board. Keep in mind that the rolling action takes a great deal of practice to master. Eventually a suitable roll can be formed which can be placed on the wall with a swift action that controls the flow of mortar into the desired position.

A bricklayer rolling mortar

A bricklayer placing a mortar roll for the basis of a wall

Placing a brick on the mortar roll

Once the mortar is in position it can be distributed as necessary along the length of the wall by a spreading action with the back and tip of the trowel blade. With practice the thickness of the mortar can be accurately judged so that, when a brick is placed, it will not need to be hammered into position and there will be no *excessive* mortar squeezed from the joint.

The following step by steps show spreading a bed joint.

STEP 1 Place the brick in the wall.

STEP 2 Remove the excess mortar from the joint.

STEP 3 Apply mortar to the next brick.

STEP 4 Insert and remove mortar from the header face.

Remember, this is a real skill that requires much practice and repetition. Surplus mortar squeezed from the bed joint must be removed with care. The final appearance of the work can be spoiled if mortar is smudged over the face of the wall and not cut off carefully.

PERP JOINTS

Forming a perp or cross joint is also something that requires continuous practice. With the brick held almost vertically in one hand and the trowel in the other, a suitable amount of mortar is picked up and spread on the header face of the brick. There are a number of techniques to achieve this, but it should always be remembered that the practice of 'wiping' a small amount of mortar on the front and back edges of the header face will not produce a weatherproof joint. Good standards of workmanship demand that perp joints and bed joints should be **full**.

The following series of steps show one method of forming a full perp joint.

Be careful when removing excess mortar. Smudged mortar doesn't look good!

STEP 1 Apply a small amount of mortar to the header face of the brick.

STEP 2 Use the trowel to make a smooth joint.

Full

In this context, it means that the joint has no gaps or voids that will allow water penetration

ACTIVITY

If your house or your friend's house is built of brick, do you notice mortar smudged on the face of the wall? Look around for examples of 'clean' walls and note how much better they appear.

STEP 3 Angle the brick to smooth each side of the joint.

STEP 4 Make sure that the joint is full.

GETTING STARTED

Building brickwork in the workshop is obviously different from producing a piece of work on site. The workshop is an indoor environment and therefore has none of the weather considerations that working outdoors brings with it.

In addition, in the training workshop we build on a reasonably level surface – the floor. On a building site, however, it's probably true to say that we will never find a *perfectly* level surface to build on.

On site the bricklayer is often called upon to build on uneven concrete foundations. This calls for particular skills to build his or her work up to specified levels above ground level. In Chapter 2 you will learn how the bricklayer uses datum points and bench marks to achieve this, see page 47.

For now we'll concentrate on dealing with how to build straight walling and corners in half-brick or Stretcher bond in the training workshop. We will assume that our wall is designed to whole brick dimensions, so there will be no need to reverse the bond or to cut bricks to produce broken bond, as described in the previous section.

STEPS TO SUCCESS

Although a workshop floor may appear to be level, there will undoubtedly be small variations from point to point. We therefore need to begin by making sure that our first course is laid level from end to end. There are a number of ways to achieve this.

One method is as follows:

1 Mark the two end points of the wall in accordance with instructions. The marks could be in chalk or a thin spread of mortar marked with a line made with the point of the trowel to indicate the required dimension. (Note: You may decide to set out the first course dry to ensure uniform joint sizes will be achieved, as already discussed.)

2 Lay a brick on a mortar bed at both ends of the wall to correspond with the marks. Try to line them up with each other by eye for now. The beds should be 10mm, but may need to be adjusted as we'll see in a moment.

3 Since the wall is likely to be longer than the length of a spirit level, we will need to use a straight edge to 'transfer' a level reference from one end of the wall to the other. Our spirit level is placed on top of the straight edge so that we can now level over a greater distance.

4 We will now probably need to make adjustments to *one* of the bedded bricks. Checking the spirit level will tell us whether we need to raise or lower one brick to make it level with the other. We could also place our straight edge against the face of the bricks to line them up more accurately with each other.

5 When we are satisfied that the laid bricks are level with each other, we can attach a string line (line and pins) to the top face arris at each end. We now have an accurate level reference to lay the rest of the first course to.

The following step by steps show the key points in the method for laying out a level first course.

STEP 1 Mark the two ends of the wall.

STEP 2 Lay a brick on a mortar bed at both ends.

STEP 3 Use a straight edge to check the bricks are level.

STEP 4 Use the spirit level to confirm a level wall.

STEP 5 Attach using a string and line.

A bricklayer is not the only tradesperson who uses a straight edge. Think about what other trades might use a straight edge and write down what jobs they would use them for. Think about where an operative would use a straight edge when looking in 'Our House'.

Attaching a line to the two isolated bricks can pose problems. A string line needs to be as tight as possible. We don't want it to sag in the middle since our course of brickwork would follow the sag and would look unacceptable. However, if we pull the line too tight, it could dislodge our carefully positioned bricks. Getting the tension right is something that comes with experience. A little later, we will look at attaching our line and pins to the brickwork we build at each end of a wall.

Here is one method of attaching the string line to our two isolated bricks:

Using line and pins to set out

Using a dead man to create a temporary profile

Another method is to use temporary 'profiles' such as a concrete block placed on end to which we attach our line. Because the block is heavier than a brick, we can pull the attached line much tighter. Some bricklayers refer to a temporary brick or block used in this way as a 'dead man'.

If our design of wall is simply a straight run of bricks without corners, our next step is to build a rack either end. *Racking back* is the term used to describe the process of stepping each course laid at the ends of a wall to produce a plumb reference point that guides accurate laying of the rest of the wall. Since the wall doesn't **return** around a corner but has a straight end, we will need to introduce a half-bat in alternate courses to maintain Stretcher bond (or half-bond).

Return

The expression used in brickwork to describe the portion of brickwork at right-angles to the face of the wall

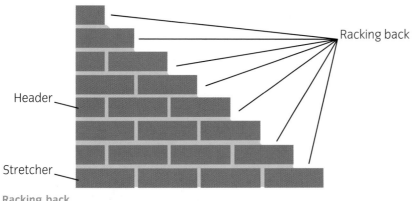

Racking back

Header

Stretcher

Racking back

The thickness of each bed joint in the rack is kept uniform and accurate to make sure that the final height of the wall is kept to specification. This is known as keeping to **gauge** and requires frequent checking with a tape measure. Sometimes it will be easier to use a gauge rod. This is a timber rod with shallow gauge markings made on it with a saw. On site it has the advantage of including markings to show heights of specified levels such as window sills.

Half-bonded brick rack

Gauge

The dimensions of a bed joint (10mm) and a brick depth (65mm) added together (75mm)

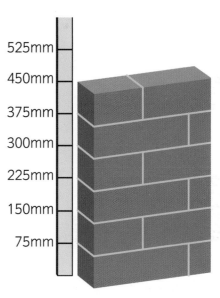

525mm
450mm
375mm
300mm
225mm
150mm
75mm

Keeping to gauge

Let's say that you are laying the first course of your rack four bricks long. Having laid and prepared your bed of mortar, you might at first lay one brick at a time and level it before laying the next brick. This is fine to begin with, but over time you will develop the confidence to lay all four of the bricks (or however many are in that course) and level them in one operation.

As you improve your skills, building a rack is faster and more accurate if you follow a simple sequence:

- gauge
- level
- plumb
- line.

ACTIVITY

If the gauge measurement for one course of brickwork is 75mm, work out what the gauge measurement will be for
1 9 courses
2 15 courses

Answers: 1) 675mm, 2) 1125mm

Note: Checking the *gauge* measurement can be done when the first brick is laid and levelled at the corner point, or when the whole course is completed and levelled.

So, first *level* the four bricks we have laid, then *plumb* each end of the course, and finally *line* in the face of the four bricks between the points you have just plumbed.

Level

Plumb

Line

These three procedures are accomplished with the spirit level in hand, which speeds up production. Once we have accurately built our brick racks at each end of our wall we are ready to fill in the masonry between them. We need to use our line and pins again but now we add another simple but effective tool to our toolkit – a corner block.

CORNER BLOCKS

Corner blocks are made of plastic or wood and use the tension of the string line stretched from end to end to keep them in position. They are easy to make from timber available on site. They make it quick and easy to adjust the string line up the wall for each course of brickwork to be laid.

OUR HOUSE

Look online at a building tool supplier website (start with Buck & Hickman.) Check out the types of corner blocks that they sell. Look at the corner blocks in 'Our House' too, as an additional guide to how the blocks should appear.

THE CITY & GUILDS TEXTBOOK

Having considered how we set out and build a straight wall, let's look at how we set out a wall that has corners specified for the design. In brickwork, a corner has an unusual name: a quoin. A corner or quoin, is usually set out as a right-angle; in other words it is set out at 90°. (There are quoins set out to other angles that you will learn about as you progress to higher levels.) In Chapter 3 you will find more details about setting out squares and rectangles using a number of methods.

In the training workshop we are most likely to use a steel square to set out our brickwork. Care and accuracy are once again the main requirements. Having set out and laid our first course as already described, we place one leg of the steel square against the face of the first course to create an accurate angle for our return to follow.

After we have laid our return bricks we need to ensure that they are level. Always level from the corner point to the end of the course you are laying.

This applies to each course we lay as we build our quoin to the intended height. Laying and levelling from the corner point maintains accuracy. If we keep in mind the sequence already mentioned for building a brick rack, we can speed up our work rate and add to our efficiency. Remember:

- gauge

- level

- plumb

- line.

Let's review some techniques that help us maintain quality and standards.

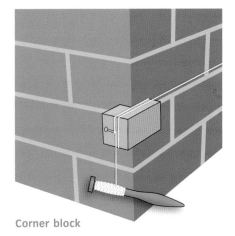

Corner block

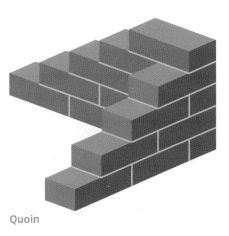

Quoin

BRICKLAYING TECHNIQUES

LEVELLING

Keep in mind that the spirit level is a precision instrument. *Never strike the spirit level to align bricks horizontally.*

Place the spirit level on the top of the course of bricks to be levelled, and gently tap the bricks, *not* the level as shown in the illustration.

If we need to make excessive adjustments, it could be that we will need to remove bricks in that course and adjust the thickness of the bed joint. Think of the quoin (or corner) brick as a 'control point' to which we refer for the rest of each course.

Spirit level being used to level top course of brickwork

PLUMBING

When only one course is laid, it is virtually impossible to plumb it accurately. Start careful plumbing from the second course. To keep the spirit level stable, place your foot against the bottom of the level whilst holding the top of the level with your free hand. Carefully adjust the bricks at either end of a course and look down the face of the wall to make sure it lines up with the spirit level. When making adjustments, once again, *never strike the spirit level to plumb a quoin.*

ACTIVITY

Check out some tool catalogues online and find out how much a *quality* spirit level costs. What's the most expensive level you can find?

Spirit level held plumb against brickwork

LINING IN

Lining the face of bricks between the plumbed ends of each course will help to produce a wall that has an accurate **face plane**. Rest the edge of the spirit level against the face of the bricks in each course. (We don't refer to any of the bubbles in the level – we just use the level as a straight edge.) Gently tap the bricks into line. *Never strike the spirit level to line up a course.*

Face plane

The alignment of all the bricks in the face of a wall to give a uniform flat appearance

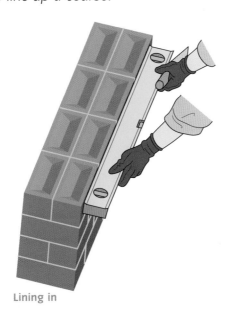

Lining in

RANGING

An accurate face plane will also be achieved if we *range* our work. This again means using our spirit level as a straight edge, but this time we place it in line with the stepped brickwork as it racks back. (This applies to a straight rack as well as a quoin.) Gently tap the bricks to align them with the edge of the spirit level. *Never strike the spirit level to range a quoin.*

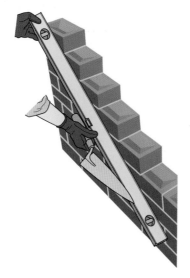

Using a spirit level diagonally

With any of these operations, if we have to strike the brickwork with force to bring it accurately into line, then we may need to pay more attention to how we place and spread mortar and how we lay the bricks. Remember – we are brick *laying* not brick *bashing*!

LAYING TO THE LINE

When we are satisfied that our quoins are completed accurately, we can use them as a guide to 'run in' the walling between the corners or racks. Laying to the line is another aspect of bricklaying that needs time to develop speed and accuracy. The main points to keep in mind are:

- Make sure the top arris of the brick is level with the line along the full length of the brick.

- Never lay the bricks touching the line. Doing this will cause the line to move away from the face of the wall and will result in a curved face plane. Keep the top arris of the brick about the thickness of the line away from the line.

- 'Eye' down the wall to ensure the face plane is smooth and the perps are lined up vertically.

FINISHING THE WALL

Finally we need to consider the finishing of the wall. The bed and perp joints need to be **tooled** or **ironed** in order to satisfy two requirements:

- to produce the desired appearance that is specified

- to weatherproof the joint in order to prevent the entry of moisture.

The most commonly used joint is called a half-round joint. A specific tool called a jointer is used to produce a concave finish to the mortar just before it begins to harden. The timing of the operation is very important since if it's performed too soon it will lead to a rough finish and if it's performed too late a black deposit will sometimes form due to what is known as lime burn.

Because the profile of the half-round joint is concave, the procedure of jointing pushes the mortar tight against the arris of the brick and seals it against moisture penetration.

It's good practice to joint all the perps first, followed by the bed joints. This reduces the number of small projections where the perp joint and the bed joint **intersect**.

Tooled or ironed

This refers to the procedure using steel tools to create a specified type of joint

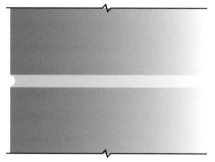

Half-round joint

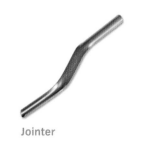

Jointer

Intersect

To pass through or across

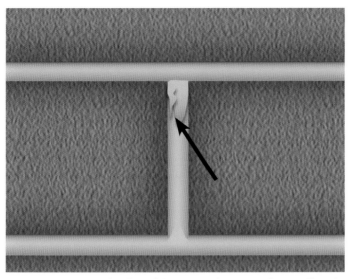

'Mouse ears' or 'curtains' on brickwork jointing. These are the small projections which occur when the horizontal and vertical joints intersect

INDUSTRY TIP

The half-round joint is also commonly referred to as a 'bucket handle' joint. This is because the shaped handle found on old metal buckets was used to form joints in the past.

ACTIVITY

Check out some examples of brickwork as you travel around and look closely at the jointing. Do you see any holes or voids in the work? If moisture is allowed to get into the brickwork, what effect do you think it will have?

A good bricklayer is constantly observant, looking for flaws in the bricks he or she is laying and discarding materials that may affect the quality of finish. Brickwork can be knocked and nudged by other workers nearby, so check the work frequently to maintain plumb and level. Be critical of your own work and aim to constantly improve your own standards, and employers and customers will always be happy to give you work.

BUILD STRAIGHT BRICK WALLING AND RETURN CORNERS IN ONE-BRICK WALLING TO THE GIVEN INSTRUCTIONS

As previously mentioned, one-brick walling is brickwork built to produce walling with a width of 215mm – the length of one brick. This means that bricks can be laid across the wall as well as in line with the wall. The bricks laid across the wall are called headers, and the bricks in line with the wall are called stretchers, because of the relevant faces of the brick showing in the finished wall.

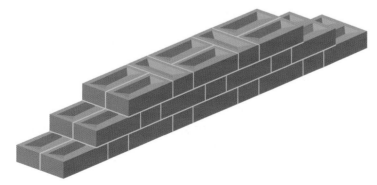

Finished wall showing headers and stretchers

A wall built to this thickness is obviously stronger than a half-brick wall and will usually be used in situations that require greater strength, such as:

■ walls carrying steelwork

■ inspection chambers

■ fire walls

■ free-standing walls used as garden or boundary walls.

The two main bonds that are built as one-brick walling have been referred to already — Flemish bond and English bond. These bonding arrangement provide a lap of a quarter of a brick.

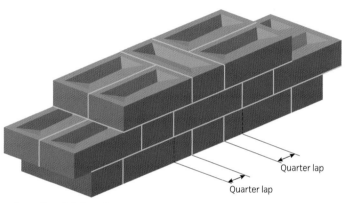
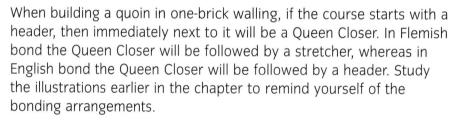

Quarter lap in a Flemish bond

One-brick wall having a bed spread along it

When building a quoin in one-brick walling, if the course starts with a header, then immediately next to it will be a Queen Closer. In Flemish bond the Queen Closer will be followed by a stretcher, whereas in English bond the Queen Closer will be followed by a header. Study the illustrations earlier in the chapter to remind yourself of the bonding arrangements.

Although the wall is thicker than half-brick walling, the techniques used in forming bed and perp joints are similar. We still need to prepare the mortar by rolling it ready for spreading but, we need to be aware that we will produce a shorter bed joint in one movement of the trowel, owing to the increased width of the wall. With practice a larger amount of mortar can be rolled and picked up from the spot board to speed up the work rate, but remember this takes lots of practice.

When perping the stretcher face of a brick (to lay a brick in a course of headers), our perps will obviously be longer. The temptation may be to 'top and tail' the perp by just placing mortar on the ends of the stretcher face. The skilled bricklayer aims to produce a full joint with mortar placed along the full length of the face of the brick. This will ensure a weatherproof joint to contribute to a long-lasting and durable wall.

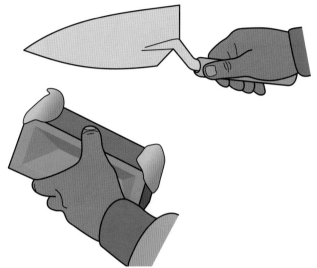

Header being perped using top and tail method

INDUSTRY TIP

Some bricklayers prefer to treat a one-brick-wide wall as two half-brick walls back-to-back when spreading the bed joint. In other words, they lay two thinner beds side by side.

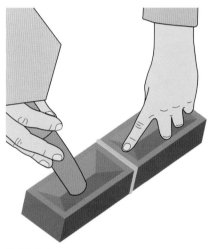

Full joint

TYPES OF ONE-BRICK BONDS

Let's look at the differences in these one-brick bonds.

FLEMISH BOND

The bonding arrangement of Flemish bond basically consists of alternating headers and stretchers within a course. The headers in a course are centred above the stretchers in the course below to give a strong Quarter bond and also to produce an interesting pattern.

Flemish bond is often specified because it has a decorative pattern that is acceptable on both sides of the wall. Think about it – we've already talked about the fact that bricks can vary slightly in size. That being the case, if we lay a header brick to the line (as described for stretchers in the previous section), whilst the face of the brick will be accurate, the other end of the brick will vary in the amount it projects compared to other headers in the wall.

Longer bricks project more from the back of the wall

Centre line

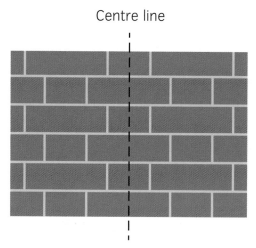

A decorative pattern on a Flemish bond wall

Fair-face

Indicating face work of neat appearance

Elevation

Any face of a building or wall

Lateral

From the side

Since Flemish bond has fewer headers in the bonding arrangement, our wall is more likely to have a better appearance on both sides. The back of this type of wall is often referred to as '**fair-faced**'.

ENGLISH BOND

This bond is set out with alternating courses of headers and stretchers. Since English bond has more headers showing in an **elevation**, it is not so suitable for use where good appearance is desired on both sides of the wall. However, the bonding arrangement makes English bond the strongest bonding arrangement possible.

That's why it is often specified for situations where the brickwork may have to withstand a lot of **lateral** pressure, for example in an inspection chamber where the weight of the surrounding subsoil presses in on the masonry.

English bond brickwork

LAYING TO THE LINE

With one-brick walling, we could say that the width of the wall is the same as two half-brick walls laid back to back with a 10mm joint between them. If we are building the equivalent of two walls, do we need two string lines to produce accurate work?

To produce high-quality work, some bricklayers will decide to use two lines; one on the face and the other on the fair-face (or back line of the wall). The face side line is used as described already, but the fair-face line can only be used to establish *level* and not line. This is because the header bricks will vary slightly in length and so can't be laid accurately to both lines.

Two strings in use: one on the front edge and one on the back edge

The usual practice is to lay the header with its rear arris very slightly below the line, so as not to push the rear line out of alignment with the run of the wall.

Building one-brick walling uses greater quantities of materials and places greater demands on operatives in preparation of the work area. It requires the bricklayer to use similar techniques to those needed to produce half-brick walling, but with a few modifications to allow for increased proportions.

FORM JUNCTIONS IN BRICK WALLS TO THE GIVEN INSTRUCTIONS

There are many points in a building or other structure where one wall intersects with another to form a **junction**. One example would be where the partition walls in a house (walls between rooms) meet the outside walls. The junction is formed by bonding the masonry to form a stable and strong feature.

Junction

Where two walls meet at an intersection

Partition/party wall adjoining outside cavity wall

Indent

A recess formed in the brickwork

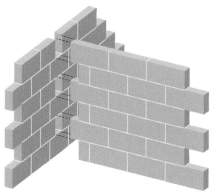

Indents in blockwork

CHOOSING THE METHOD

There are a number of ways that the masonry could be bonded for stability. The choice of method will depend on factors such as access requirements and the planned sequence of work. If building a wall that joins another wall would block off easy access to a part of the building, then the method chosen could be to leave **indents** in the main wall.

These are holes or pockets accurately formed in the wall at each course or block of courses as building proceeds. The indents are the width of the wall that will be built later, with allowance for a mortar joint either side of the added wall, to make sure that the junction is solid and stable.

A simpler way of providing for a junction wall at a later stage is to use reinforcing mesh. This is carefully built into the bed joints on the vertical line of the wall that will be added later. The mesh is built in as work on the main wall proceeds, in accordance with site instructions and specifications.

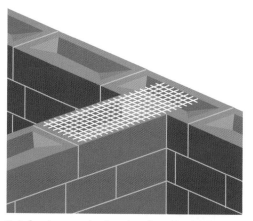

Reinforcing mesh showing from bed joint

If there are no issues related to access and no other problems are foreseen, then the junction wall can be built along with the main wall course for course. The overlap or bond of the junction should follow the overlap of the walls being built. In other words, if the walls are one brick thick, then the lap or bond should be a quarter of a brick and if they are half-brick walls, then the lap should be half-bond.

Sometimes a junction wall may be added at a later date after the main wall has been completed, perhaps owing to a change in design. In this case indents may need to be cut out carefully to allow the new wall to be attached. When cutting holes in masonry, use the right tools that have been maintained in a safe condition, and remember the importance of using the correct PPE.

Indents cut out to receive the new wall

A more modern approach to forming a stable junction between walls is to use **proprietary** connectors or wall starter kits.

Proprietary wall starter kit

Proprietary

Manufactured and sold under a brand name or trademark

ACTIVITY

Check out the CATNIC website and look for 'stronghold wall starter kits'. Find out what the benefits of using this type of system are.

Case Study: Josh and Sid

Josh had been working for a small building company for about six months as an apprentice bricklayer. He had been partnered with Sid, an older, more experienced bricklayer who knew the trade inside out.

Sid was good at explaining things and Josh felt he was making good progress in developing the skills he had learned at college. Sid kept emphasising the need to think carefully about each task and plan ahead. That way, you can help to avoid problems later on.

The company had a contract to produce decorative brickwork in solid walling for a new retail park. The work required special bricks to be ordered. Josh was keen to try his hand at some of the fancy brickwork, but Sid said he should be patient and 'get the basics right first'.

When the special bricks for the job arrived on site, Sid was in the manager's office. Josh decided to supervise the delivery and picked a good storage location, somewhere the bricks wouldn't be damaged. He told Sid that the delivery was sorted and gave the site manager the paperwork.

After wet weather held the job up, the time came to start the feature work using the special bricks that Josh had previously taken delivery of. He arranged with the forklift driver to transport the first pack of bricks to the work area.

When they arrived, Sid was upset. 'You didn't cover them when you took delivery — we can't lay wet bricks!'

Josh remembered what Sid kept saying: 'get the basics right first'.

Work through the following questions to check your learning.

1   When building even levelled courses, the wall is

   a   Gauged

   b   Staged

   c   Caged

   d   Coursed

2   Which of the following is a recognised bond?

   a   Full bond

   b   Stop bond

   c   Turned bond

   d   Reverse bond

3   If a wall does not work full bricks, the bond is called a

   a   Damaged bond

   b   Broken bond

   c   Full bond

   d   Half bond

4   A bricklayer will bond the bricks for

   a   Decoration

   b   Colour

   c   Cost

   d   Strength

5   The wastage allowance for brickwork is

   a   5%

   b   10%

   c   15%

   d   30%

6   Communicating with the line manager is best carried out

   a   By letter

   b   By phone

   c   Using text

   d   Verbally

7   The action to take upon an incorrect delivery of bricks is to contact the

   a   Supplier

   b   Architect

   c   Line manager

   d   Client

8   Technical details on a working drawing can be located in the

   a   Specification

   b   Bill of quantities

   c   Contract

   d   Email

9   When is a bricklayer required to wear PPE?

   a   Never

   b   Always

   c   Important events

   d   Sometimes

10   Bricklayers use dry bonding to establish the

   a   Joints

   b   Face

   c   Correct bond

   d   Ranging

11 The total number of bricks to build a wall 3.0 high by 3.0m in length, with a thickness of 102.5mm is

  a 510

  b 520

  c 530

  d 540

12 Four pallets of bricks each containing 390 bricks are delivered to site, 10% are damaged. How many bricks are being returned?

  a 102

  b 120

  c 130

  d 156

13 What is the name of the smallest cut brick inserted into the middle of a wall?

  a Quarter brick

  b Half-bat

  c Three quarter bat

  d Bevelled brick

14 The rules of bonding requires the quoin header to be followed by a

  a Header

  b Stretcher

  c Queen Closer

  d Three quarter

15 Perp and bed joint should be

  a 5mm

  b 10mm

  c 15mm

  d 20mm

16 What procedure will ensure a flat surface?

  a Range the wall

  b Plumb the wall

  c Level the wall

  d Gauge the wall

17 The term 'perps' relate to the

  a Long bed joints

  b Short vertical joint between bricks

  c Ends of a bed joint

  d Cross joint of the wall

18 The term 'header' relates to the

  a Length of the brick

  b Width of the brick

  c End face of a brick

  d Arris of a brick

19 The term 'bucket handle' relates to the

  a Bucket with no handle

  b Type of brick

  c Form of joint finish

  d Tool used for jointing

20 The term 'indents' refers to

  a An apprentice's qualification papers

  b The dips in a rough concrete foundation

  c Pockets left in a wall to allow another wall to be joined

  d Marks on the surface of a metal tool

Chapter 5
Unit 103: Carrying out blocklaying activities

Concrete blocks are an essential material for building walls and this chapter explains how you will use them in the brickwork trade. In this chapter you will learn about blockwork and the relationship between dense (heavy) blocks and lightweight insulation blocks. Bricklayers use a range of blocks: this chapter will cover the standard sized block, which is 440mm in length, 215mm in height and 100mm thick.

By reading this chapter you will know how to:

1 Prepare for blocklaying activities in accordance with work specifications.

2 Use dense concrete blocks and lightweight insulation blocks to build block walling to given specifications.

PREPARING FOR BLOCKLAYING ACTIVITIES

SOURCES OF INFORMATION

As a bricklayer you will be given a variety of written instructions, including:

- working drawings

- **CAD drawings**

- emails

- facsimiles (faxes)

- specifications

- bill of quantities.

CAD drawings

Drawings created from computer-aided design software

Working drawings

Understanding the areas on a working drawing is made easier by following the hatching symbols. See Chapter 2 page 48 for more examples of hatching symbols. The symbol for blockwork (abbreviated to BLK) is:

INDUSTRY TIP

In drawings, break lines in walls indicate that the walls continue above and below.

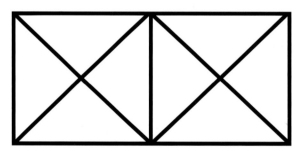

CAD drawings

Bricklayers use a range of different drawings. The drawings are produced mainly by hand and drawn by an architect. Large jobs can command up to 20 different sheets of drawings, and this is where computer aided design (CAD) comes into its own. Using a computer to produce drawings allows the architect to change, alter, take out and add diagrams and dimensions at any time. This ability to make changes stops the need to start the drawing again if drawn by hand.

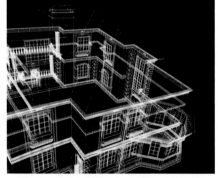

CAD drawing for a property

Emails and facsimiles faxes

Using emails and faxes within construction is common. Bricklayers can and do use smart phones to send and forward emails, not only for the workforce but also to communicate with material suppliers. See Chapter 2 for more details.

Specifications

The specification should be checked to find out details about the type of blocks and the type of joint finish that will be used. Again, more detail on specifications is available in Chapter 2, page 51.

Bill of quantities

The bill of quantities requires the builder to add together the different materials and come up with a price to undertake the job. The bill is a document created by the quantity surveyor detailing all materials and areas where the different resources are used. It's down to the bricklayer to look at the total areas of brick and blockwork and price accordingly. See Chapter 2, page 54, for more details about this.

DEALING WITH POTENTIAL HAZARDS

Using blocks can be very dangerous. The size, weight and make-up of the block can lead to accidents.

Risk assessments and method statements

You must complete and follow risk assessments when undertaking all of the tasks involved in the job. The method statement will give written details about each task. Once you know the hazards for each task you will be able to put control measures in place. See the HASAWA 1974 in Chapter 1, pages 4–7.

Manufacturer's instructions

Most block manufacturers provide online or printed instructions on the use of their product. You must always follow them.

PPE

Bricklayers endure common accidents while building, such as bricks and blocks dropping on to feet and toes, small cuts to fingers and hands, and inhaling dust from a working site. The PPE used helps to eliminate the degree of crushed toes, cuts to hands and the amount of particles inhaled.

Always wear the correct PPE when handling blocks, as listed in the risk assessment. You must wear the following PPE when building block walling. For full details about what PPE should be worn on site, See Chapter 1, pages 20–23.

Overalls

Goggles

Gloves

Safety helmet

Safety boots

Hi-vis jacket

Falls

Many health and safety issues must be addressed when preparing to work at height to avoid falls and other accidents, for example when loading resources on to access equipment. For more information see the section about Work at Height Regulations 2005 in Chapter 1, pages 24–30.

Blockwork performed at height should make use of working platforms

TOOLS AND EQUIPMENT

Cutting and fixing blocks uses all of the traditional tools a bricklayer will carry in their tool box or bucket.

TOOLS

The table below shows the tools you will need to build block walling and explains their use.

Tool	Description and use
Laying trowel	A trowel for laying both bed and perp end joints.
Pointing trowel	A trowel for filling bed and perp ends. It is also used to form a finish to the face joint.
Tape measure	A measuring tool for bricklayers to determine the length of a wall or building.
Gauge rod	A rod made from timber or metal with stepped markings of 75mm, to help maintain the gauge in height for **courses** of bricks.
Club hammer	A weighted hammer used to cut bricks and blocks.

Course

A horizontal row of blocks or bricks laid on a mortar bed

Tool	Description and use
Comb hammer	A hammer with metal teeth used to dress a brick or block.
Line and pins	Nylon line and metal pins used to help maintain the level of bricks and blocks.
Jointer	A shaped metal tool used to form a joint finish and shape.
Spirit level	A metal tool with built-in horizontal and vertical veils used to maintain the bricks or blocks plumb and horizontal.
Straight edge	A straight piece of metal or timber. Tool used in conjunction with a spirit level to help transfer a level.
Brick bolster	A tool used to cut bricks or blocks, shaped to a chisel point and used with the club hammer.
Builder's square	A tool used to mark corners as square when building quoins.

EQUIPMENT

As well as your tools, you will need equipment to build block walling. The table below shows the equipment you will need and explains their use.

Equipment	Description and use
Profiles	Timber frames used to fix ranging lines which represent the trench and wall widths.
Wheelbarrow	A mobile container used to transport mortar or waste products.
Shovel	A tool used to move materials and excavate ground resources.
Spot board	A flat timber or steel board used to support the blockwork mortar at intervals along the building line.
Bucket	A container used to carry water or mortar, and waste products.

PREPARING THE WORKING AREA

It is very important to prepare the working area ready for blocklaying in order to successfully complete your task. Preparation by site personnel must be included in the **programme of work**. For example, time should be allocated for preparatory tasks such as stacking and loading out the various block resources.

Programme of work

A series of events where the order of activities and the amount of time involved has been planned out. This is usually shown in the form of a bar or gantt chart.

Look at 'Our House'. What sort of blocks do you think are being used here? Where do you think they feature?

With good preparation and storage, the working area will enhance the laying of the blockwork and help to produce good quality blockwork.

Good preparation leads to good blockwork

MATERIALS

Dense concrete blocks are the cheapest type and have a range of uses. They are designed to be covered over or buried. The blocks provide strength but have little in the way of decorative finish.

Lightweight blocks are designed to be used internally, usually to insulate a house or dwelling and trap the warm air within the structure. A **cladding** finish, eg **render** or plasterboard, usually covers lightweight blocks to provide a finished surface.

The images below show the most commonly used blocks:

Dense

Material that is hard and heavy

Cladded

When a surface is covered in another material

Rendered

When a brick, stone or block face is covered in a layer of sand and cement

Lightweight block

Dense block

Stacking blocks

Block manufacturers deliver blocks to sites in a safe manner by placing the blocks on pallets and wrapping in sealant or holding them in place with **straps**. This makes it easier for the delivery driver to position and stack the blocks.

The positioning of delivered materials is very important. The site compound or storage area needs to be close to the designated work area and to the front entrance.

Blocks must be stacked no more than 1.8m or two stacks, or pallets, high. This allows the site machinery to pick them up and transport them. It also means that site personnel can access and load the materials into wheelbarrows. Site personnel can load out very near to the working area and, if possible, the stacks of blocks should mirror the positions of the bricks. The most common form of stacking blocks is the bonding arrangement shown below, known as four on four.

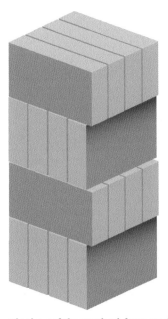

Blocks safely stacked four on four

The loading of blocks close to the spot board and working area should be uniform. Spot boards hold the mortar, and are raised up from ground level by supporting the board on blocks. Along the line of the wall there should be alternate stacks of blocks and spot boards to allow you to continuously lay along the full length of the wall you are building. See Chapter 4, page 138 for information on this arrangement for bricklaying.

Straps

Plastic binding holding bricks or blocks together on a pallet

Pallets of blocks

INDUSTRY TIP

Always fold up the straps from the stacks of blocks or bricks and dispose of them safely. The straps are dangerous and can cut hands or legs.

INDUSTRY TIP

Always check the bottom row of blocks for cracks or other damage. These blocks are under greater pressure during storage and are usually the first to break and fall on your foot when they are lifted.

INDUSTRY TIP

Four blocks stacked upright are equal to the length of one block. Remembering this will enable you to place a dry, stacked column of blocks square and tidily next to the spot board.

Spot boards of mortar, alternating with stacks of blocks

Lifting and carrying materials

Always read the risk assessment prior to handling the materials. The movement of blocks must be kept down to a minimum to stop **double handling**.

The cause of most accidents when handling blocks is an operative lifting a block by hand, not realising that the block is split or broken and the block falling apart in their hands and onto their feet. You must always check the condition of a block before you lift it.

As you know, blocks are categorised as either lightweight or dense. This means you will be handling either lightweight or heavy resources. It makes sense to use machinery when handling heavy materials and, as discussed, not to stack the columns too high. Otherwise you might create a risk when the block is carried to its laid position.

Protecting materials

Protecting the blocks before, during and after a day's work is very important. Blocks delivered to site are wrapped for protection. The wrapping protects against water and contamination of soil. Pallets are supplied to also help keep the blocks off the ground for the same reason.

Sand can be protected by delivering to site in 1 tonne bags or metal skips. The reason for this is to protect against sand spreading across the mixing area and causing contamination.

How to calculate resources

When calculating the number of blocks required the **rule of thumb** is 10 blocks per 1m². This can help when storing blocks next to the working area and when calculating the number of blocks laid in a day. The standard block size is 440mm in length, 215mm in height, and 100mm in width.

Double handling

Moving materials twice or even three times before use

Rule of thumb

Industry recognised practice

When calculating the number of blocks you will need for a straight wall, the rule of thumb is the length of two blocks (440mm x 2) plus the perp joint (12mm) rounded up equals 900mm. So, two blocks for every 900mm, four blocks for every 1.8m. Remembering this will help you to calculate quantities and wall sizes.

SETTING OUT

The setting out stage is when you locate the position of building works ready for starting work. This is the time to mark from the profiles to the over site slab or foundations. It is also when you consider the bonding of the blockwork, which is the arrangement of blocks that spreads the load through the wall. Setting out and measuring given lengths and calculating the number of blocks is important.

Prior to building brick or block walls the setting out has to be completed; this involves setting out the first two courses without mortar, known as dry bonding. The dry state allows the bricklayer to establish the correct bond, and for the positioning of the stopped ends and perp ends to be marked on the foundation.

Dry perp joint

TYPES OF BOND

Stretcher bond (half-bond) is the most common type of bond used by bricklayers. The bond in blockwork involves ensuring the perp joint of a block is directly in the middle of the block above.

If a length of blockwork does not work to full blocks, procedures for a **reverse bond** or **broken bond** must be put into place. Firstly, we'll look at half-bonding. **Half-bond** is the trade term for stretcher bond, see above.

Stretcher bond

The bricks or blocks are arranged with an overlap the width of a brick or block. This means the perp joints are exactly halfway along the face of the stretchers in the course below

Reverse bond

In the same course, starting with a stretcher bond and ending with a header

Broken bond

The use of part bricks to make good a bonding pattern where full bricks will not fit in

Half-bond

Stretcher bond (half-bond) is the most common type of bond used by bricklayers. The bond in blockwork involves ensuring the perp joint of a block is directly in the middle of the block above

HALF-BOND

Bonding of blockwork normally follows a half-bond (stretcher) pattern. The use of a 100mm cut at the quoin on alternative courses will maintain the bond.

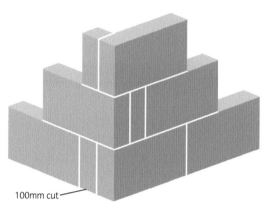

100mm cut

Block quoin showing a 100mm cut

ACTIVITY

Calculating linear measurement within blockwork uses a tape measure. Knowing how many blocks fit in to a measurement is key.

How many blocks are needed to make a linear length of 3.6m?

Answer: 3.6m ÷ 0.45 = 8 blocks

REVERSE BOND

This bond starts with a full block and finishes with a half block on the same course.

Full block

Half block

Reverse bond

BROKEN BOND

When measuring for blockwork, if the block will not fit, a cut has to be inserted. Placing cut bricks within a course of brickwork is called broken bond. The smallest cut allowed is known as a **half-bat** and measures 215mm without a perp (the same size as the header face of a full block).

INDUSTRY TIP

If a wall has a broken bond, always ensure the bonding arrangement is set out over the first two courses and continued under a door or window opening.

Broken bond

Cut blocks in broken bond should be placed as near to the centre of the wall as possible. If there are doors or windows in the wall, the broken bond can be placed underneath one of them. When a half-bat is built into a course of blockwork, the course above and below it will contain two three-quarter cuts (or bats) to maintain the bond.

Broken bond under a window

Temporary profiles

Timber frames made from rails and pegs positioned on the boundary of a plot to fix ranging lines

TEMPORARY PROFILES

Using **temporary profiles** to help support the blockwork can make it easier to build a greater height of walling.

Temporary profiles are used and positioned to support blockwork. The blockwork can be constructed to a greater height. The profiles are usually made from timber and inserted at intervals along the length of the wall and fixed or wedged from floor to ceiling; this allows the bricklayer to rest and support the blocks during the build.

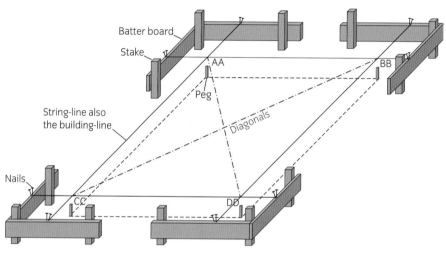

Temporary profile

HOW TO CUT BLOCKS

When cutting blocks the bricklayer must adopt the same procedures as for cutting bricks; the block should be cut into two halves with minimum waste. These cut blocks will help maintain the bond when laid. The lightweight blocks can be cut using a hand saw – not a carpentry saw but a masonry saw. See pages 130–131 of Chapter 4 for the step by step guide on cutting bricks.

Masonry saw

Bolster

A broad bladed chisel used for cutting bricks and blocks

SEQUENCE OF WORK

Knowing the procedure for blocklaying is essential to producing a good result. We will now look at the procedure from start to finish.

Imagine you have been given the task of completing the inner skin (leaf) of a cavity wall using 100mm lightweight blocks.

1 Transfer building lines from profiles to slab or concrete.

2 Check corners for square.

3 Lay quoin (corner) blocks.

4 Check quoin blocks for level and plumb.

5 Build quoins, fix ties and insulation.

6 Infill blockwork.

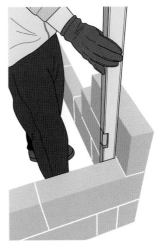

Plumbing a block quoin

HOW TO LAY BLOCKS

When laying blocks the correct procedure must be followed step by step:

1 Set out the working area.

2 Set out two courses dry and mark the bond.

3 Build the quoins.

4 Infill between the quoins.

5 Finish the blockwork joints.

The **bed joint** is applied as normal but the block must be positioned on end ready to receive the **perp joint**. All the perp joints must be full and complete. Laying the perp joint will ensure you meet the **Industrial Standards**.

Industry standards require the tradesperson to build blockwork to tolerances, for example +/- 3mm for plumbing. This means the bricklayer can have the wall plumb and vertical to within 3mm. Standards apply to all areas such as gauge, level, plumb, square and ranging.

As mentioned on page 175, setting out dry allows the bricklayer to establish the correct bond and mark the positions of all perps. The following image shows the shape and thickness of the perp joint to a block. The joint must be full and complete and to a thickness of 12mm.

INDUSTRY TIP

Working to a sequence applies to set procedures when a course of bricks or blocks has been completed. For example, always check the gauge, level, plumb and ranging in the same order. Always check your plumbing points in the same order around the wall. This will lead to good quality blockwork.

Bed joint

Continuous, horizontal mortar joint supporting the bricks

Perp joint

Small vertical joints which join two bricks together, at right angles to the bed

Industrial Standards

Minimum standards of quality of completed work

INDUSTRY TIP

When applying a perp joint to a block, apply it as you would a bed joint. This will let you form a full and complete perp joint.

INDUSTRY TIP

If the blocks are wet or damp, the overall height laid will be affected. The bricklayer may only lay four or five courses of dense blocks, or five or six lightweight blocks in bad weather. The weights of the blocks will force the water out of the joints and the wall will become unstable. Always use dry blocks.

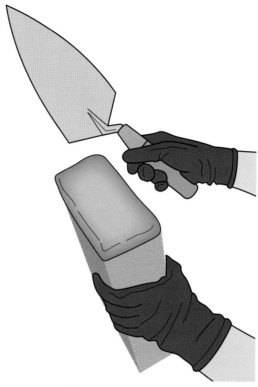

Block on end showing perp

Bricklayers could position the perp joint on the last block laid and not stand the block on end. However, this procedure will not result in a full and complete joint and therefore will not meet the Industrial Standards.

At this stage the bricklayer can put the trowel down and use two hands to lift and position the block. If infilling, the bricklayer can use a **line** at the same time. The rule of thumb on the number of lightweight blocks laid in one day is 20 to 30m². Depending on the weather conditions, the number of dense concrete blocks may be fewer.

Line

A string used to guide the blocks or bricks to make them straight

HOW TO LAY BLOCKS TO A LINE

As mentioned previously, thorough preparation before laying blocks is critical to good workmanship when building either straight or angled walls. If you spend time correctly loading out, cutting the blocks and cleaning the work area you will complete your task well.

Laying blocks to a line can be achieved by different methods. We will look at these next.

Look at the blockwork used in the foundations of 'Our House'. What methods have been used to put it together?

Weighted method

The **weighted** method uses the weight of the block itself to hold the line and provide the weight to pull the line taut.

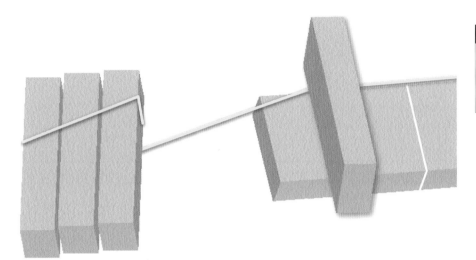

Fixed line using weighted method

Weighted

Use of dense cut block to weight down the line to stop the pulled line from moving

INDUSTRY TIP

After wrapping the line around the half concrete block always put a brick on top of it. This will help grip the line when it's pulled tight.

Line and pins method

The traditional line and pins method uses the perp joint to hold the line taut. The disadvantage of using this method is that holes are left in the perp joints when the line is moved up the wall.

Line and pins in use

INDUSTRY TIP

If possible always insert the pins into the blockwork face of the wall. Place the pins in the middle of the **stopped end** bed joint to reduce the damage to the face of the wall.

Stopped end

Vertical plumb stopped end to a wall

Corner blocks

Plastic or wooden blocks used to hold the line to a stopped end

Corner block method

Corner blocks are more commonly used when running lines of blockwork than the line and pins method. They can be made from timber or plastic and are easily moved up the wall.

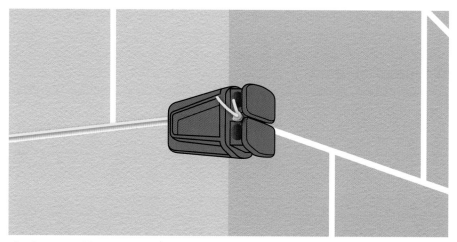

Plastic corner block in use

BUILDING STRAIGHT WALLS, ANGLED WALLS AND QUOINS

Angled

Angled walling set to angles of either 45°, 90°, or 135°

The exact sequence of activities for building straight and **angled** walls using blocks will be determined by the resources. The resources will have been specified by the client and the architect in the specification.

Building straight walls has a sequence, which includes

- establishing the bond dry
- marking the ends and perp ends
- laying the two end bricks
- fixing the line
- infilling the blockwork.

Building angled blockwork has a slightly different sequence:

- establishing the bond dry
- marking the ends and perp ends, including the position of the angle
- laying the three end bricks
- fixing the line
- infilling the blockwork.

BUILDING STRAIGHT WALLS

Building straight block walls with either dense or lightweight blocks will mean using a different method. However, the bricklayer will gauge, level, plumb and range the blockwork as normal. These procedures are the same as for brickwork (see Chapter 4, pages 149–150).

Plumbing a straight wall

BUILDING ANGLED WALLS

Angled walling ranges from 45° to 135°:

- **acute** walling is 45°

- quoin (corner) work is 90°

- and **obtuse** walling is 135°.

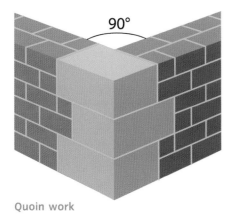

Quoin work

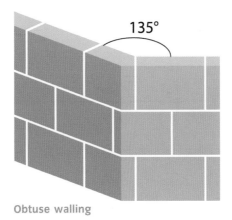

Obtuse walling

Acute

An angle less than 90° but more than 0°

Obtuse

An angle less than 180° but more than 90°

Acute Walling

For acute walling, to calculate 45° on a working drawing follow the procedure below using the image for guidance.

1 Using a compass and a pencil from Point A, make a mark on the horizontal line (we'll call this Point D).

2 Without changing the measurement on the compass, do the same for the vertical line (Point E).

3 Again, without changing the compass measurement, move your compass to Point E and draw a mark that is parallel to Point D.

4 Do the same on Point D, making a mark that is parallel to Point E. The two marks that you have created should cross over each other.

5 From the point where the two lines cross over (Point F), use a rule to draw a straight line to Point A.

6 This will give you an angle of 45°.

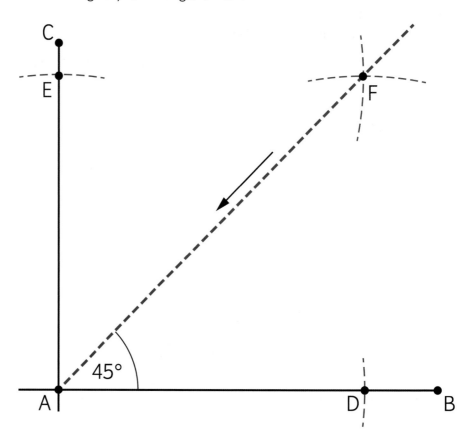

Quoin work

Obtuse walling and quoin work angles are produced on the job using the tools from the bricklayer's tool box: tape measures, a spirit level, a straight edge, pegs and a club hammer.

Building quoins (corners) has a greater degree of difficulty than solid walling because you need to use a builder's square. The corner has to be marked square prior to any blocks being laid, the square corner must be maintained for the full height of the wall and each course must be checked upon completion for square. For quoin work, to calculate 90° in the field, follow this procedure below:

1 Mark a point as Point A on the ground with a peg, and form a straight line from point A to a new point, called Point B. This line is called your base line.

2 Measure halfway along the base line to form a new point, Point C, and mark with a peg.

3 Place your builder's square at Point C with the horizontal side on the base line as shown in the drawing.

4 Mark the ground along the vertical side of square and mark a new point, Point D.

5 Between the line running from Point C to D, and from C to A, you will have a right angle. As this is the mirror of the angle from Point C to D and from C to B, you will have a right angle here as well.

Builder's square

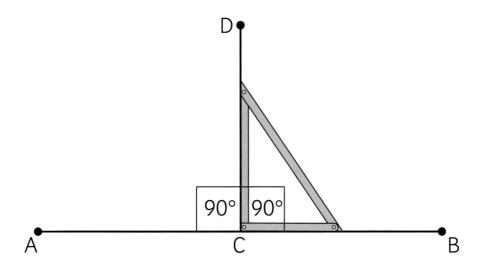

Squint brick

Obtuse walling

Obtuse walling uses specially shaped bricks called 'squint bricks' to create the 135° angled corner. For obtuse walling, to calculate 135° in the field, follow the procedure below:

1   Mark a point as Point A on the ground, and form a straight line from A to a new point, called Point B.

2   Measure halfway along this line to form a new point, Point C.

3   Place your builder's square at Point C with the horizontal side on the base line as shown in the drawing.

4   Mark the ground along the vertical side of square and mark a new point, Point D. This has formed a right angle between the lines running from Points A to C and from C to D.

5   Measure a short measurement along the base line from Point C to Point B. Call this new point Point E.

6   Transfer the length of this short measurement to the vertical line (between Points C and D) and call this Point F.

7   Transfer a line between Points E and F.

8   Measure halfway along the line between Points E and F and mark this as Point G.

9   Transfer a line from Point G to Point C. This has formed a 45° angle between Points C to D and C to G.

10 Between the line running from Point A to C, and from C to G, you will have an angle of 135°. This is because the angle between Points A to C and from C to D is 90°, and from C to D and C to G is 45°, and 45° add 90° equals 135°.

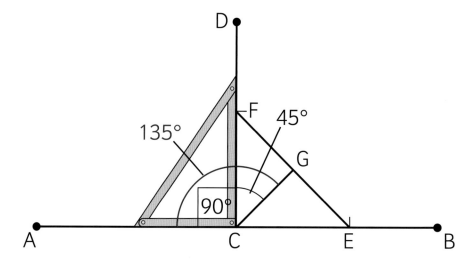

FINISHING THE WORK

Usually, blocks are covered over with brickwork, render or cladding. The industrial **tolerances** are relaxed slightly for the perp joint size. Blockwork can be +/- 15mm except for a **class A blocks**.

Class A block wall

FINISHING THE JOINTS

How you finish blockwork joints when you have completed a wall will be determined by the wall's purpose. For example, if the completed blockwork will not be displayed, or if it will be rendered or cladded; you can use a **flush joint**, which is where perp ends and bed joints are flush to the face with mortar.

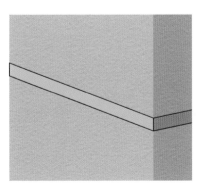

Flush joint

Tolerances

Allowable variations between the specified measurement and the actual measurement

Class A block

A high quality fair-faced block

Render coat

INDUSTRY TIP

Always joint the perps first. Next, working from the ends of the bed joints, joint into the middle of the bed. This will produce a better finish to the joint overall.

Flush joint

Bed and perp joints finished with a trowel flush to the material used

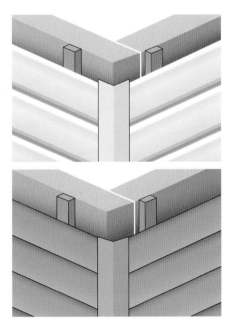

Blockwork can be protected with plastic or timber cladding

Half-round

The shape of the finished bed and perp joint

However, if the completed blockwork will be visible you will need a finished joint to the bed and perps. The most common form of joint for blockwork is a **half-round** joint, where perp ends and bed joints are finished to a half round shape. As you will remember from Chapter 4, a half-round joint is produced by running a jointer over the top surface of the bed and perp end joints. The shape of this tool is semi-circular, so running the tool through the mortar forms a concave, rounded shape to the joints. The correct procedure for producing this joint is to joint the perp ends first and then the bed joints.

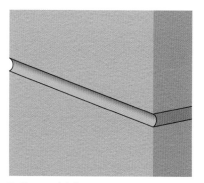

Half-round joint

PROTECTING YOUR WORK

Protecting the blocks before, during and after a day's work is very important. If bad weather is due the blockwork laid needs to be covered over with a **tarpaulin** or plastic sheeting until the mortar has hardened.

Tarpaulin

Sheet material, usually plastic, used to protect materials

Blocks covered on a site

The wind can blow and suck a wall down after it has been completed. The overall height of the wall needs to be considered and protected.

A completed and solid block wall

Case Study: Robert

Robert has been working as a bricklayer for over 35 years. He knows the difference between laying dense concrete blocks and laying lightweight insulation blocks. The position and demands made upon the blocks is all important. For example, any building work below ground level needs a dense block to carry the load of a structure. Robert has to work out the ratio of mortar to suit the type of block and its location.

At the start of a project, Robert will stack all blocks correctly, position the blocks within reach and make sure he does not have to walk too far to get hold of the mortar and blocks to construct the walling.

Next, Robert will set out two courses dry and establish the working bond, which when using blocks is a stretcher bond. Robert will check the building is square and transfer the face lines to the concrete using a level from the ranging lines. The first course will be checked diagonally for square and Robert will build the quoins first. Robert will build all quoins and then infill up to DPC level.

At DPC level Robert will source the lightweight blocks and insulation to be used. Robert is fully aware that the type of insulation will determine how the inside skin is built. Robert understands if a partial fill insulation is used, the lightweight block skin has to be built before the external skin. Methods of construction such as gauge, level, plumb, square and range have to be applied to all courses of blockwork so that Robert builds his brickwork to the same quality and height.

Having worked for many years in the UK, Robert knows how to protect his work at the end of the day, not just from wet weather but from the wind too. The use of waterproof sheeting and temporary wind supports all play a part in Robert's working day.

Work through the following questions to check your learning.

1 The abbreviation BLK stands for

    a Brickwork

    b Blockwork

    c Building

    d Boardwalk

2 What is the most common form of joint finish?

    a Weather struck

    b Weather struck and cut

    c Recess

    d Half-round

3 Which **one** of the following must a bricklayer wear when handling blocks?

    a A respirator

    b Goggles

    c Sunscreen

    d Ear plugs

4 What is the length for a standard sized block?

    a 100mm

    b 215mm

    c 330mm

    d 440mm

5 Which **one** of the following would you use to cut blocks?

    a Tape measure

    b Club hammer

    c Profile

    d Line and pins

6 What is the name of the bonding arrangement most commonly used for stacking blocks?

    a Two on two

    b Four on four

    c Six on six

    d Ten on ten

7 The rule of thumb for the number of blocks per 1m² is

    a 5 blocks

    b 10 blocks

    c 20 blocks

    d 40 blocks

8 What can a bricklayer use to cut lightweight blocks?

    a Panel saw

    b Cross cut saw

    c Hand saw

    d Masonry saw

9 Why do bricklayers use dry bonding?

    a To establish the joints

    b To establish the face

    c To establish the correct bond

    d To establish the ranging

10 What degree is the angle for obtuse walling?

    a 45°

    b 90°

    c 130°

    d 135°

11 How many blocks are needed to build a wall 3.0m high by 3.0m in length, with a wall thickness of 100mm?

    a 60 blocks

    b 70 blocks

    c 80 blocks

    d 90 blocks

12 Two pallets of blocks have been delivered to site. Each pallet contains 90 blocks, of which 15% are damaged. How many blocks will be returned?

a 25

b 26

c 27

d 28

13 What is the tool shown?

a Rod

b Pole

c Stick

d Jointer

14 What is the tool shown?

a Chisel

b Bolster

c Scrapper

d Paste knife

15 What degree is the angle for quoins?

a 25°

b 45°

c 90°

d 135°

16 What is the size blockwork joints should be?

a 10mm

b 12mm

c 15mm

d 25mm

17 What is the correct sequence?

a Level, plumb, gauge and range

b Range, gauge, level and plumb

c Plumb, level and gauge

d Gauge, level and plumb

18 What operation ensures a wall is vertical?

a Levelling

b Plumbing

c Ranging

d Squaring

19 What is the tool shown?

a Jointer

b Pointing trowel

c Gauging trowel

d Laying trowel

20 What is the most common type of bond used by bricklayers?

a Reverse bond

b Broken bond

c Stretcher bond

d Header bond

Chapter 6
Unit 105: Carrying out cavity walling activities

This chapter discusses the skills and knowledge required to carry out basic cavity walling tasks. Building cavity walls requires the use of construction methods that are more technically demanding than the methods used in the production of solid walling. Maintaining high standards of work in building cavity walling is essential. If Industrial Standards are met, the finished product will last a long time and perform its function as a major part of a structure.

By reading this chapter you will know how to:

1 Prepare for building cavity walling.
2 Build straight cavity walling and return corners.

PREPARE RESOURCES FOR BUILDING CAVITY WALLING

Cavity walls were introduced as a construction method more than 60 years ago, mainly because they give greater protection from moisture penetration than previous methods of wall construction. Years after their introduction, it was realised that they also give building designers the opportunity to allow several different types of insulation to be installed. (You will learn more about this at Level 2.) Preventing heat loss in buildings is an increasingly important aspect of building design as the drive to reduce carbon emissions continues. Previously it was normal practice to design houses and other structures using solid walls.

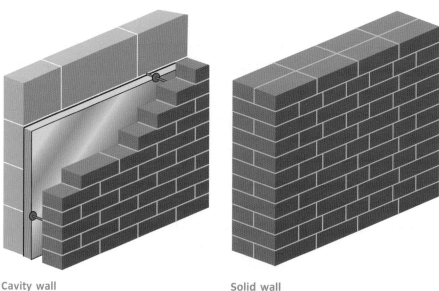

Cavity wall   Solid wall

In Chapters 4 and 5, we discussed how to build straight walling and return corners using both bricks and blocks. Getting ready to build cavity walls has many similarities since the most common arrangement for cavity walling is to build the outer skin (leaf) in brickwork and the inner skin in blockwork. You will learn more about other methods of building cavity walling at Level 2.

When you prepare resources for cavity walling, remember:

- There are 60 bricks in 1m².

- There are 10 blocks in 1m².

INDUSTRY TIP

Sometimes both skins of a cavity wall will be built in blockwork if the outside finish of the structure will be rendered.

FOLLOW THE RELEVANT HEALTH AND SAFETY REGULATIONS

Whatever type of walling we are working on, the emphasis should always be on addressing health and safety issues properly and appropriately. Risk assessments and method statements are important documents which assist all workers, whether on site or in the training workshop, to be safe from injury or even death (see Chapter 1, pages 5–6). Take them seriously!

Also remember that many materials used in construction are potentially hazardous. Always take note of the manufacturer's directions and technical guidance on how to use products safely and make sure you consult the relevant COSHH statements (see Chapter 1, pages 9–11).

In Chapter 1 we discussed a range of health and safety legislation relating to the construction industry, such as HASAWA 1974 and the Work at Height Regulations 2005. You need to be familiar with these regulations as a great deal of a bricklayer's work is performed above ground level on scaffold of one type or another.

Because greater attention has been given to health and safety matters there has been a large reduction in the number of injuries and deaths in the construction industry. This improvement can only be maintained if everyone pays careful attention to the safety and welfare of ourselves and those working around us. Get into the habit of thinking about how you're going to minimise hazards before you start laying bricks or blocks.

For example, some cavity wall designs will require lightweight insulation blocks that are easy to handle and cut, but generate a lot of dust. So when you select your PPE for a task using insulation blocks you need to consider how you can protect yourself and others from dust contamination, eg by using goggles or safety glasses and a dust mask.

A health and safety inspector at work

INDUSTRY TIP

Get into the habit of checking the packaging of materials you are using for useful health and safety information.

Lightweight insulation block

OUR HOUSE

Use an internet search engine to find some block manufacturers' websites. Try searching for 'Thermalite®' as a starting point. Look for the manufacturers' product guides. Try to find out what lightweight insulation blocks are made of and where they would be used in 'Our House'.

Other cavity wall designs may specify dense concrete blocks in the structure, so not only do you need to select the right PPE (in this case safety boots, gloves etc), you also need to be aware of the risk of injury if you don't use proper lifting and handling techniques (see Chapter 1, pages 18–19).

Later in this chapter we will discuss wall ties, which are an essential part of cavity wall construction, but can also be a hazard. Whichever skin or leaf of a cavity wall that we build first, there will always be wall ties projecting from it that can potentially cause injury as we build the second skin.

Safe bricklayers start looking ahead and planning how they will deal with things like this when they pick up a working drawing or a specification. It's a good idea to write a list of the PPE you will need for a particular work task. You must always check that it is in good condition. If it's not in good condition and safe to use, report this to your line manager or supervisor and use a new item.

It's also good to find out about the Building Regulations for masonry design so that you can understand why things are built the way they are.

Damaged PPE like these gloves and goggles should be replaced

USEFUL REMINDERS

Preparation of resources for the successful construction of cavity walling is all about careful planning, especially since cavity walling is more complex to build than solid walling.

Much of what has already been discussed in Chapters 4 and 5 on block and bricklaying regarding preparing resources also applies to building cavity walling, so review these chapters.

Here are some of those important points and how they relate to cavity wall construction.

Check that the materials are the correct specification and are undamaged

The wrong bricks may not be suitable for the location and conditions in which the cavity wall is being built. The wrong blocks may have inadequate strength or **thermal** insulation properties.

Damaged bricks or blocks can affect the appearance of finished work as well as reducing the strength and **durability** of cavity walls.

Understand and work to the relevant information sources

Make sure you fully understand the instructions for the work to be carried out. Whether you are working in the training workshop or on a construction site, one of the main methods of communicating information is through a working drawing. Understanding the drawing symbols and hatchings used on the drawing is essential in order to produce the work as specified (see Chapter 2, page 48).

Thermal

When material, such as insulation, is designed to keep heat in

Durability

How capable a product is of withstanding wear and tear or decay

INDUSTRY TIP

The correct width of a brick is 102.5mm.

A working drawing being consulted

If the drawings or written instructions are not easy for you to understand, ask your supervisor or line manager to discuss them with you.

Keep the work clean and protect it from damage

The finish provided by face brickwork can be permanently scarred by carelessness. Blockwork can be relatively fragile until the mortar sets hard, so it can easily be pushed out of plumb or line. Good bricklayers think about potential damage to their work by other construction operations and poor weather conditions.

Support sustainability

When waste is created by cutting operations, always dispose of the waste properly and keep a clean and safe work space (see Chapter 4 for details on cutting by hand). Recycle waste whenever possible to support **sustainability**.

Sustainability

To continue to do something with minimal long-term effects on the environment

Site waste being properly disposed of

ACTIVITY

Make a list of the main tools a bricklayer uses (no more than five or six). Write down the potential dangers they could cause if they're not properly maintained.

Damaged tape measure

Common bricks

Bricks of medium quality used for ordinary walling work where no special face finish is required. They may be covered or hidden

Check that you have enough materials for the job before you start

Make a list of the resources that will be required. Running out of materials causes delays and costs money. Having excessive materials creates unnecessary work when the materials have to be moved after the job is completed. Review the methods of calculating area and linear measurements in Chapter 4, pages 133–135.

Check that the tools and equipment are appropriate and safe to use

Check the condition of your tools and equipment before you use them. Using tools that are not in a safe condition can cause accidents. Something as simple as a hammer can be extremely dangerous, if the head is loose it could fly off and strike someone. Maintaining your tools properly keeps you, and those working around you, safe and will also make the tools last longer.

SET OUT TO BUILD CAVITY WALLING TO GIVEN INSTRUCTIONS

After carefully identifying, preparing and checking your resources for cavity walling, you can now go about the task of setting out your work area and positioning the materials and components ready for the building stage. Once again you need to give careful consideration to health and safety matters, in particular, the Manual Handling Operations Regulations 1992 (see Chapter 1, pages 17–19).

MATERIALS

When cavity walls were first introduced, they were often built using brick for the inner and outer skins. The outer skin would be built in face brick and the inner skin would be built using **common bricks**. The modern approach allows a range of bricks to be used for the outer skin.

The bricks used may be manufactured from:

- clay
- clay and shale
- concrete
- sand and lime.

Some designs will specify dense concrete blocks for the outer skin and occasionally concrete blocks can also be used for the inner skin. However, it's more usual to construct the inner skin in lightweight insulation blocks. The choice usually depends on the type of insulation to be used. You will learn more about this at Level 2.

Remember that bricks and blocks are heavy components and need to be moved and handled with care. This is especially the case with dense concrete blocks. It's very easy to cause injury to your hands and fingers by trapping them between the heavy blocks when stacking them. If blocks are handled roughly they can sometimes develop a **fracture** that is not easy to see. Then, when the block is lifted at the ends it may break into two or more heavy pieces which can fall and injure an operative's legs or feet. So, remember that careful handling and being observant are very important.

Fracture

A crack or break in a hard object or material

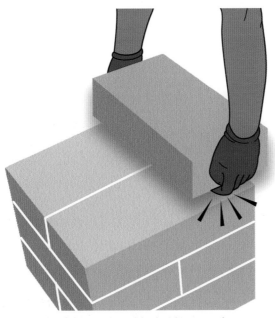

Be careful when stacking blocks that you don't trap your fingers

ACTIVITY

Use an internet search engine to search for 'brick tongs'. Identify the highest and lowest prices you can find for this item.

INDUSTRY TIP

If you're stacking out materials at ground level, take some time to level off the ground you're stacking on. If you're stacking out materials on scaffolding, never stack higher than the hand rail.

Stacks of bricks can be positioned on edge with two rows of six bricks in each layer, up to 12 layers in each stack. It's a good idea to discuss how high you should stack bricks and blocks in particular locations with your supervisor or a more experienced bricklayer. They can often direct you to guidance provided by manufacturers and health and safety regulations that apply to handling and positioning masonry components and materials competently and safely.

Tools for moving bricks manually such as brick tongs are designed to comfortably carry six bricks at a time to minimise the risk of damage to the materials and injury to the operative. Dense concrete blocks are best moved one at a time if moved by hand.

Bricks stacked properly

Use a forklift to move heavy materials

Air bricks

A perforated building block to allow ventilation through walls

Whenever possible, arrange to move all heavy masonry components by using mechanical handling methods such as a forklift or crane. The operators of these machines are trained in safe working practices, so cooperate with their directions and be alert at all times.

In previous chapters we discussed how to set out the materials in relation to the wall that is going to be built. In the case of solid walling, there are usually only two materials to consider; either bricks and mortar or blocks and mortar.

With cavity walling however, you will have to position three materials: bricks, blocks and mortar. (You will also need to set out insulation, wall ties and damp proof course and occasionally **air bricks** which are built into cavity walls to vent specific parts of the structure. For now let's concentrate on the heavy materials.) You could position a stack of bricks next to a stack of blocks next to a spot board of mortar along the length of the wall, repeating the pattern around the quoins (or corners).

Stacks of bricks and spot boards on a site

Another way would be to position combined stacks of bricks and blocks alternating between spot boards. The way these are stacked is determined by which skin (or leaf) of masonry will be built first. If the block skin is built first then the bottom part of the stack would contain bricks with blocks stacked on top ready for laying. If the brick skin is built first then the bottom part of the stack would contain blocks with the bricks positioned on top ready for laying.

Stacks of blocks and bricks being used to build a cavity wall on a site

Whichever method is used, it is important to calculate the amount of required materials in order to cut down on unnecessary movement of heavy materials, ie double handling.

Remember that the distance that materials are placed from the wall that is going to be built is important for efficient working. Usually, stacks of materials and spot boards for mortar should be placed around 600mm from the **face** line of the wall.

SETTING OUT

The sequence of steps used to set out masonry in brickwork or blockwork is discussed in detail in Chapters 4 and 5. When building cavity walling, the same principles of care and accuracy apply. You need to take great care to make sure that your first courses of brickwork and blockwork are level, to the required line and to the correct overall dimensions.

You will remember from Chapter 4 that setting out dry is helpful in establishing the correct bond within the given dimensions for all types of masonry construction. It also helps you to decide whether you need to cut bricks and blocks or reverse the bond (see Chapter 4, page 140) in order to make things fit within the design dimensions.

There is an additional dimension to consider when setting out cavity walling. This is the specified distance between the two masonry skins that form the cavity. This dimension will vary according to the design of the structure and whether or not insulation is to be built into the cavity design. In the past the width of the cavity was usually between 50mm and 75mm, but with the more frequent use of insulation in the cavity, the dimension is often increased to a width of 100mm.

Face

The surface presented to view; the front

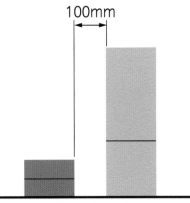

First course of a cavity wall

By ensuring that the first courses in a cavity wall are set out accurately, it will be easier to maintain high standards throughout the rest of the construction process. Frequently checking that the work is maintained level, plumb and to the correct gauge and dimensions is an important way of avoiding expensive problems at later stages in the construction process.

An operative checking his work

Maintaining high industrial standards is also important from a safety point of view. For example, official guidance provided by the BSI (BS EN 1996-3:2006) states that a single wall in a cavity wall design should not be built higher than:

- 6 courses of blocks or

- 18 courses of bricks.

Stabilise

To support or hold steady

Before building any higher, the other wall of the cavity design must be built to the same height in order to **stabilise** the cavity structure. Think about it – if we didn't follow this guidance and we built too high, we would risk having the free-standing wall being blown over by a strong gust of wind, possibly with us and others in the way.

Carefully setting out the work area and the masonry task prior to actually commencing cavity wall construction supports a number of important factors. Setting out:

- maintains safe practice both in the training workshop and on site

- adds to efficiency and productivity

- maintains the Industrial Standards.

BUILD STRAIGHT CAVITY WALLING AND RETURN CORNERS TO THE GIVEN INSTRUCTIONS

A cavity wall is more complex to build than a solid wall. Since a cavity wall is wider at the base than 215mm wide solid walling, and consequently has lighter loadings, there must be greater care in the design to deal with movement and cracking. In addition, the inner skin, or leaf, of a cavity wall usually supports the weight of the floors and roof of a structure, so the design has to withstand the downward pressure created by this weight.

The care taken in construction design must be carried through to the building stage by the bricklayer. If good trade practice is not consistently employed, the cavity wall is less likely to fulfil its intended purposes of:

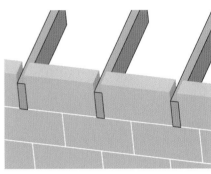

Floor joists supported by inner skin of cavity walling

- supporting the dead loads of the floors and roof, transferring them safely to the foundation

- maintaining structural stability

- resisting wind loadings

- preventing moisture penetration into the interior of the structure

- insulating against heat loss.

DAMP PROOF COURSE

As mentioned at the start of the chapter, one of the main reasons for using cavity walling is that it is more effective in preventing moisture penetration into the living or working area of a structure than solid walling.

The following images illustrate how moisture can travel through a solid wall, causing damp, and how a cavity wall prevents moisture entering the structure.

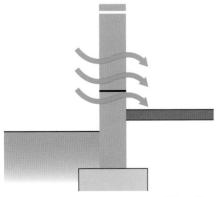

Moisture travelling across a solid wall into the dwelling

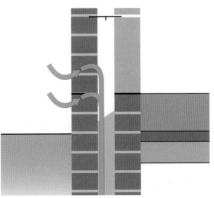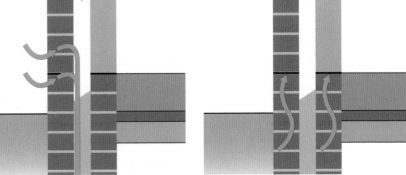

A cavity wall preventing penetrating damp (left) and rising damp (right)

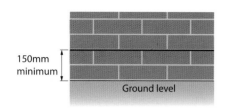

DPC outside ground level

Void

An open space or a break in continuity

ACTIVITY

Make a simple table to compare the advantages and disadvantages of engineering bricks (rigid DPC) and polythene (flexible DPC). Discuss your comparisons with another student.

Engineering bricks

Hard dense bricks of regular size used for carrying heavy loads, eg in bridge buildings and heavy foundations

Polythene DPC

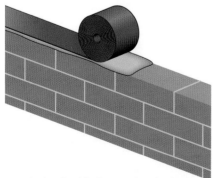

DPC being bedded on a thin bed of mortar

Preventing damp in a building is important for two reasons:

1 Damp affects the health of the occupants.

2 Damp causes the fabric of a building to deteriorate.

If the main reason for using cavity wall construction in a building design is to prevent the entry of moisture into the living area, why do we need to build a damp proof course (DPC) into a cavity wall?

The reason is that moisture passes through masonry in all directions: if vertically, it is called rising damp, and if horizontally, it is called penetrating damp. This is due to capillary attraction – a process that draws water into the tiny **voids** that exist in masonry materials. To break the path of water travelling vertically from below, a barrier in the form of a DPC is introduced into both skins of a cavity wall at a minimum of 150mm above finished ground (or path) level.

The DPC at this location is referred to as a horizontal DPC and usually corresponds to fixed floor level (FFL). DPC is also installed around door and window openings in cavity walls where the inner skin meets the outer skin to close the cavity at reveals. This is referred to as vertical DPC. You will learn more about this type of DPC at Level 2.

MATERIALS USED

The materials used for DPC fall into two categories:

- rigid
- flexible.

Some examples of rigid DPC are slate and **engineering bricks**.

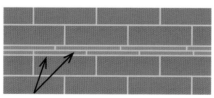

Two courses of slate bonded and bedded in mortar

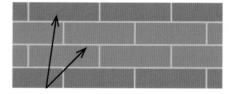

Rows of engineering bricks as DPC

Some examples of flexible DPC are polythene and pitch polymer.

INSTALL DAMP PROOF COURSES WITH CARE

Careful installation of DPC is essential to avoid problems developing later in the life of the building, which can be expensive to put right. When installing horizontal DPC at FFL the bricklayer should provide a thin mortar bed below it. This is to prevent possible damage to the DPC by hardened mortar in the brickwork opposite, which may project slightly above the surface of the brickwork.

The masonry is then built on a thin bed of mortar above the DPC taking care not to puncture it.

If a roll of DPC is too short to completely cover a section of wall, an additional roll should be laid to overlap the first section by a minimum of 100mm.

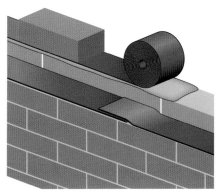

Placing bricks at intervals of 1m

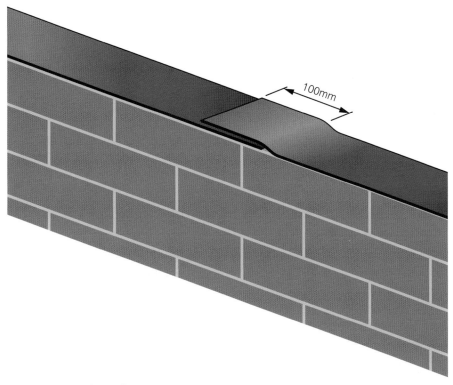

DPC being overlapped

An exception to this is when wider DPC is used. Then the overlap should be the same as the width of the DPC being used. So, 150mm wide DPC will have an overlap of 150mm.

DPC should never be allowed to project into the cavity area because mortar droppings can build up, allowing moisture to track across the cavity into the interior of the building.

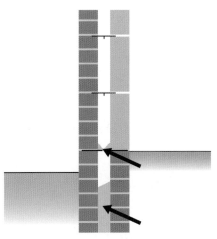

DPC projecting into the cavity wall with mortar build up

Storage

The successful installation of an effective DPC begins with the correct storage of the DPC materials. They must be stored so as to avoid tearing or puncturing. Rolls of material should be stored on end to avoid distortion and no more than three rolls high. DPCs containing bitumen and other **thermoplastic materials** should be stored away from direct heat.

Some DPC materials, such as bitumen felt, become stiff in cold weather and can crack when the bricklayer attempts to unroll them, so they should be stored in a warm place.

Thermoplastic materials

Materials which become soft when heated and hard when cooled

DPC stacked three rolls high

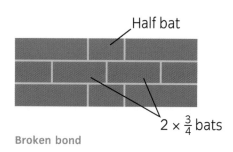

Half bat

$2 \times \frac{3}{4}$ bats

Broken bond

SUPERSTRUCTURE

The section of a building built above the DPC is called the superstructure. We can follow many of the principles for solid walling that we've already discussed in previous chapters when building cavity walling in the superstructure.

Here are some of the main points to remember.

Set out the facework bond in the outer skin accurately and carefully

Facing brickwork provides the finish of most cavity walls. Setting out the bond carefully will produce a good looking job from the floor level to the roof. If bricks have to be cut to build the wall within given dimensions, producing broken bond, try to place the cut bricks under a door or window (see Chapter 4, page 140).

Build quoins accurately and carefully, maintaining level, plumb, line and gauge

Inaccurate quoins will make it difficult to build a wall with an acceptable face-plane. The appearance of the wall will be spoiled, especially when the sun or a street light casts a shadow across the wall.

Fill all your bed joints and perp joints fully as the bricks (or blocks) are laid

Not carefully filling joints, particularly perp joints or cross joints, will allow the penetration of rain and moisture through the outer skin of masonry. Think about it – there are about 60 cross joints per 1m² of facework so not filling the joints in properly means rain can enter and damage the masonry.

Keep the cavity clear of mortar droppings and other obstructions

Developing good habits when spreading mortar beds will prevent mortar dropping into the cavity.

This is of great importance in maintaining high standards of work. Mortar dropping down the cavity can build up above the DPC and allow moisture to pass across the cavity into the living or working area. A number of methods can be employed to assist with keeping the cavity clean.

One method is to use a cavity batten. This is simply a timber batten slightly narrower than the cavity dimension with cords or wires attached. It rests in the cavity on the wall ties (see the following section) to catch mortar droppings and can be withdrawn as the work progresses using the cords or wires. The caught mortar can then be reused or disposed of.

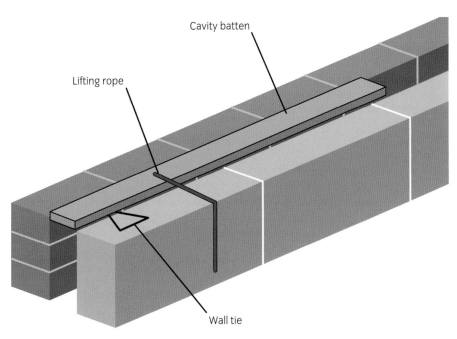

Cavity batten

Lifting rope

Cavity batten

Wall tie

Cavity batten

Another method is to leave out a number of bricks, at or just below DPC level, to allow mortar droppings to be removed before the mortar hardens. These openings, every four bricks or so, are called core holes. Alternatively, the bricks for the core holes could be laid in sand for easy removal when required.

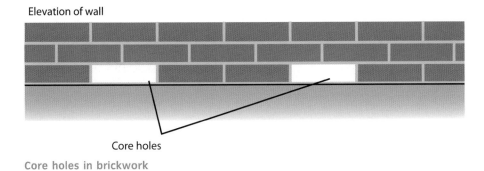

Elevation of wall

Core holes

Core holes in brickwork

WALL TIES

In Chapter 4 we discussed how to build one-brick solid walling in two bonds: Flemish bond and English bond. Remember that the bonding arrangement for both of these bonds included header bricks that ran across the width of the wall. One-brick walling is more or less the same width as two half-brick walls side by side. The headers in the bonding arrangement tie these two half-brick walls together for strength and stability.

It follows then, that if we have cavity walling consisting of masonry skins separated by a cavity, we would need some means of tying the separate skins together in order to provide sufficient strength and stability.

Header bricks tying a solid wall together

That strength and stability is provided by wall ties which are built into the bed joints of both skins and cross the cavity at specified spacing throughout the wall.

Cavity wall with ties correctly positioned

ENSURE WALL TIES ARE INSTALLED PROPERLY AND IN THE CORRECT POSITIONS

The correct position of wall ties in a cavity wall is specified in the Building Regulations and the masonry Code of Practice. The following image shows the correct spacing of wall ties.

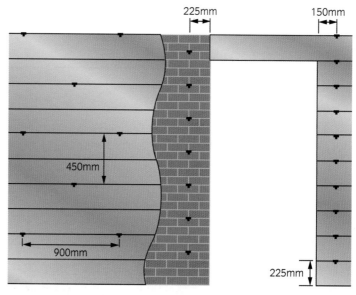

Correct position of wall ties

There are several different shapes and sizes of wall ties available which are designed to suit different widths of cavity. Also, in a multi-storey structure, the loads carried by the cavity wall will increase and so a wall tie capable of dealing with the increased loads would be specified.

OUR HOUSE

Research different designs of cavity wall ties. (Hint: Type 'cavity wall ties' into a search engine and look for two manufacturers: Catnic® and Ancon®). Take a look at the wall ties in 'Our House' to see where they go.

Wall ties are now made from stainless steel. They were previously made from **galvanised** mild steel and sometimes plastic. They have a twist or 'drip' in the centre to allow moisture that may have penetrated the outer skin to drop off in the centre of the cavity, instead of tracking across the tie into the inner skin. If moisture was allowed to enter the inner skin of masonry, it could progress into the living or working area with undesirable consequences, ie causing damp.

Galvanised

When iron or steel is covered with a protective zinc coating

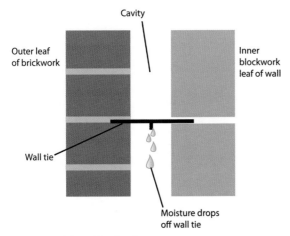

Wall tie with a drip in the centre

Damp damage inside a building

WORK CAREFULLY AT ALL TIMES SO THAT THE COMPLETED CAVITY WALL WILL ACCOMPLISH ITS PURPOSE

As mentioned previously, mortar droppings falling down the cavity must be prevented from building up at the bottom of the cavity, so that moisture cannot travel across the cavity and into the living or working area of a structure. Mortar droppings can also build up on wall ties and provide a bridge across the cavity along which moisture can travel.

Bricklayers need to pay close attention to keeping the cavity clean. If mortar does fall down the cavity you must take steps to clean it out.

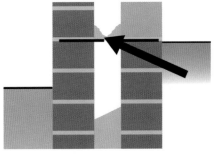

Dirty wall ties

FINISHING THE WALL

The selection of a particular type of brick for the face of the wall will influence the choice of joint finish. For example, sand and lime bricks are quite soft and would not be suited to using a recessed or racked-out joint. This is because moisture may lie on the arris (any straight sharp edge of a brick formed by the junction of two faces) of the bricks which could lead to frost damage.

It is therefore wise, if sand and lime bricks are used, to select a joint that throws moisture off the face of the wall such as a half-round or weather-struck joint.

Whatever joint finish is selected, it's the bricklayer's responsibility to ensure that the completed work meets the specification and has a good appearance without defects.

Take care in finishing your work carefully and you will produce masonry that not only looks good but will also stand the test of time.

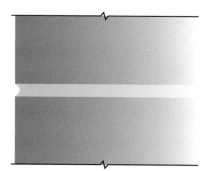

Frost damaged brickwork

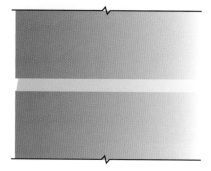

Half-round joint

Weather-struck joint

Quality brickwork

Case Study: Steve

Steve is working as an 'improver' on the site of a large house builder. His supervisor has teamed him up with another young bricklayer who is keen to earn good wages. Together they have been instructed to finish a section of first floor cavity walling on the end elevation of a detached house.

The inner skin of the wall has to be built first in dense concrete block, which has already been loaded out for them, so Steve's workmate thinks this is a great opportunity to get a lot of work done today. Steve is a bit worried by the fact that it's a breezy day and suggests that they should only build the wall five courses high before lunch.

Things go well and they finish the five courses fifteen minutes before lunch time, so Steve's workmate insists that they could manage another course of block to which Steve reluctantly agrees. They finish the extra course of block and feeling pleased with themselves they go for a sandwich.

Their lunch time conversation is interrupted by a dull thud coming from the area of the house they are working on. When they return to the work area they see what has caused it.

A strong gust of wind has blown the six courses of heavy blockwork over and has broken some of the timber beams for the floor. The supervisor is not happy and gives them some good advice: 'Pay attention to the official guidance on best practice. Don't be tempted to build higher than you should to earn more money as you could end up losing out.'

Work through the following questions to check your learning.

1 What should a bricklayer wear when cutting lightweight blocks?

   a Dust mask

   b Ear plugs

   c Disposable gloves

   d Hard hat

2 Which **one** of the following documents contains technical information that is useful to a bricklayer?

   a Newspapers

   b Building Regulations

   c A health and safety booklet

   d Posters in the canteen

3 Health and safety on site or in the workshop is the responsibility of whom?

   a Your line manager

   b The architect

   c The bricklayer

   d Everyone

4 Which **one** of the following walls would best resist moisture penetration?

   a Straight

   b Solid

   c Thin

   d Cavity

5 What is the correct width of a brick?

   a 100mm

   b 102.5mm

   c 105.2mm

   d 115mm

6 How many blocks are there in 1m²?

   a 10

   b 12

   c 15

   d 60

7 What is the total number of blocks needed to build a wall 3m high by 3m in length with a wall thickness of 100mm?

   a 35

   b 50

   c 60

   d 90

8 What is the best distance to position materials from the face line of a wall?

   a 500mm

   b 600mm

   c 900mm

   d 1000mm

9 Two pallets of bricks have been delivered to site. Each pallet contains 120 bricks, of which 15% are damaged. How many bricks are being returned?

   a 32

   b 34

   c 36

   d 38

10 Which of the following pieces of legislation applies to lifting heavy materials?

   a Building Regulations

   b COSHH 2002

   c RIDDOR 1995

   d Manual Handling Operations Regulations 1992

11 Which area of a building is described as the superstructure?

a Above DPC

b Below DPC

c On the ground floor

d On the second floor

12 What is meant by the arris of a brick?

a Colour

b Strength

c Edge

d Holes in a brick

13 Which **one** of the following can be used as a horizontal DPC?

a Cork

b Slate

c Plasterboard

d Polystyrene

14 If an engineering brick is used as a horizontal DPC, it is referred to as a

a Tough DPC

b Rigid DPC

c Solid DPC

d Hard DPC

15 If 100mm wide polythene DPC is used, any joins should be overlapped by a minimum of what?

a 100mm

b 150mm

c 200mm

d 220mm

16 What are modern wall ties made from?

a Galvanised steel

b Stainless steel

c Plastic bars

d Plastic strips

17 What is the main reason for preventing mortar from dropping into the cavity?

a To save on materials

b To make the cavity wall lighter

c To prevent moisture entering the building

d To improve the appearance of the cavity wall

18 What is the purpose of wall ties?

a To prevent materials from falling down the cavity

b To tie the two skins of a cavity wall together

c To allow cavity battens to be used properly

d To speed up the rate of work

19 Rolls of flexible DPC should be stored on end no more than

a 3 rolls high

b 6 rolls high

c 9 rolls high

d 12 rolls high

20 What is the minimum height above finished ground level for installation of a horizontal DPC?

a 100mm

b 150mm

c 200mm

d 250mm

TEST YOUR KNOWLEDGE ANSWERS

Chapter 1: Unit 201

1 c Risk assessment
2 d Blue circle
3 b Oxygen
4 a CO_2
5 b Control of Substances Hazardous to Health (COSHH) Regulations 2002
6 c 75°
7 c Glasses, hearing protection and dust mask
8 d Respirator
9 a 410V
10 b 80db (a)

Chapter 2: Unit 101

1 c 15m
2 a Open to interpretation
3 b A section through a part of the structure
4 a Strip
5 c Raft
6 c Damp proof course
7 d Polystyrene
8 d Cement
9 b 10°
10 a Foundations

Chapter 3: Unit 102

1 b Block plan
2 a Longest side of a right angle triangle
3 d Mouse ears
4 c Datum point
5 d Half-round
6 a Brickwork
7 a Full size

8 b 3:4:5
9 d Furniture
10 b Aggregates
11 a Water level
12 a Builder's square
13 a Risk assessment
14 d Jointer
15 b Builder's line
16 c Perp joint
17 a Specification
18 d 10m
19 b Optical level
20 c As large as possible

Chapter 4: Unit 104

1 a Gauged
2 d Reverse bond
3 b Broken bond
4 d Strength
5 a 5%
6 d Verbally
7 c Line manager
8 a Specification
9 b Always
10 c Correct bond
11 d 540
12 d 156
13 b Half-bat
14 c Queen Closer
15 b 10mm
16 a Range the wall
17 b Short vertical joint between bricks
18 c End face of a brick

19 c Form of joint finish

20 c Marks on the surface of a metal tool

Chapter 5: Unit 103

1 b Blockwork

2 d Half-round

3 b Goggles

4 d 440mm

5 b Club hammer

6 b Four on four

7 b 10 blocks

8 d Masonry saw

9 c To establish the correct bond

10 d 135°

11 d 90 blocks

12 c 27

13 d Jointer

14 b Bolster

15 b 45°

16 b 12mm

17 d Gauge, level and plumb

18 b Plumbing

19 d Laying trowel

20 c Stretcher bond

Chapter 6: Unit 105

1 a Dust mask

2 b Building Regulations

3 d Everyone

4 d Cavity

5 b 102.5mm

6 a 10

7 d 90

8 b 600mm

9 c 36

10 d Manual Handling Operations Regulations 1992

11 a Above DPC

12 c Edge

13 b Slate

14 b Rigid DPC

15 a 100mm

16 b Stainless steel

17 c To prevent moisture entering the building

18 b To tie the two skins of a cavity wall together

19 a 3 rolls high

20 b 150mm

INDEX

PICTURE CREDITS

Every effort has been made to acknowledge all copyright holders as below and the publishers will, if notified, correct any errors in future editions.

Access Products Ltd: p25; **Axminster Tools:** pp xvi, xvii, xx, xxv, xxvii, xxviii, xxxi, xxxii, xxxiii, xxxiv, xxxv, 20, 22, 23, 34, 36, 107, 113, 114, 115, 121, 123, 124, 126, 127, 132, 136, 154, 168, 169, 170, 171, 185, 192; **City & Guilds:** p90; **Construction Photography:** © Adrian Greeman pp xxviii, xxxii, 21, 56, 129; © Adrian Sherratt pp xxii, 89, 122; © BuildPix pp11, 33, 168, 193; © Chris Henderson pp xxvi, 34, 120, 133, 211; © CJP p89; © Damian Gillie pp85, 143, 162, 183, 200, 202; © David Burrows pp xi, xxvii, 85; © David Potter pp xiv, 92, 209; © David Stewart-Smith p91; © Grant Smith pp13, 106; © imagebroker p89; © Image Source pp15, 16, 85, 119; © Jean-Francois Cardella pp xxi, 31, 129; © QA Photos/Jim Byrne p85; © Simon Turner p30; © Steve Aland pp xxxi, 120, 137, 187; © Tom Lee pp xxxiv, 197; © Xavier de Canto pp xx, 1, 132, 210; **Direct Builders Merchants Ltd:** p186; **Everbuild Building Products Limited:** pp xxix, 132; **Fireco Ltd**: p40; **Fotolia:** © Alan Stockdale p39; **Hackney Community College:** pp x, xv, xvi, xviii, xix, xx, xxvi, xxvii, xxix, xxxii, xxxv, 34, 108, 125, 130, 131, 136, 139, 144, 145, 146, 147, 148, 150, 152, 196; **Hawes Plant Hire:** p18; **Health and Safety Executive:** pp xiv, xxxv, 9, 10, 11, 12; **If Images:** © Michael Grant pp xxviii, 47; **iStock Photo:** © Banks Photos pp 95; **Mediscan:** pp22, 23; **metals4u.co.uk:** p178; **Meteor Electrical:** p35; **Mike Jones:** pp152, 199, 201, 210; **PAT Training Services Ltd:** p37; **Pavilion Construction Ltd:** p189; **pavingexpert.com**: p91; **RIBA Product Selector:** pp xxvii, 79; **Shutterstock:** © 29-Sept p16; © 3DDock pp xvii, 166; © alessandro0770 p93; © Alena Brozova pp xxv, 95; © AlexRoz p171; ©Alexander Erdbeer p13; © Anton Foltin p24; © antos777 p43; © aragami12345s p 18; © auremar pp18, 45, 65, 75, 190; © Barry Barnes p41; © Bokic Bojan p46; © Brian A Jackson, p120; © Bronwyn Photo p xv; © Chad McDermott p xv; © Cynthia Farmer p18; © Dainis pp172, 195; © Darkking p15; © daseaford pp41, 200; © dekede pp xv, 138; © DeiMosz p42; © DenisNata p22; © Dermarcomedia p15; © DmitriMaruta p90; © Dmitry Kalinovsky pp31, 60; © Donald P Oehman p198; © Feng Yu p120; © Ford Photography p42; © Goodluz p197; © Grushin p xviii; © Gustav pp xxxiii, 58, 136; © gyn9037 p xxxii; © Igor Sokolov (breeze) p3; © Igor Stramyk p xxxv; © imageegami pp xviii, 132© Israel Hervas Bengochea p25; © Jahina_Photography p91; © Jakub Cejpek p102; © Jesus Keller p97; © John Kasawa p95; © JP Chretien p83; © Julija Sapic p128; © Kaspri p41; © kavalenkau p37; © Kekyalyaynen p91; © Ken Wolter p172; © koleg pp xxviii, 173; © Kraska p23; © kzww p74; © Krzysztof Slusarczyk pp xxx, 89; © Laitr Keiows p xxi; © Lost Mountain Studio p171; © Lorenzo Mondo pp xviii, 187; © Mark Humphreys p89; © Michael Vigliotti p93; © mike.irwin p16; © Monkey Business Images pp69, 166; © MrSegui p87; © Mr.Zach p39; © Naiyyer p23; © Natalia Siverina p xxiii; © objectsforall p18; © Olegusk xxxvi; © Paul Wishart p77; © Pavzyuk Svitlana p93; © Perig p93; © Phisekit p15; © photobank.ch p63; © Photodiem p101; © Phuriphat p15; © Pressmaster pp xiv128; © pryzmat pp82, 93; © Rafael Fernandez Torres p15; © sbarabu p36; © Sergej Razvodovskij p xxvii; © smereka p93; © Smileus p96; © Stephen Finn p77; © Stephen Rees pp xx, xxxiv172, 188; © StockCube p195; © stocksolutions pp xiv, 59; © SueC p95; © Susan Law Cain pp89, 137; © Terry Kent p90; © titov dmitriy p93; © TonyV3112 p77; © Treenoot p132; © Tribalium p42; © trufero p91; © T.W. van Urk p xxxi; © Viktorus p74; © windu pp xxi, 78; © woaiss p xxvi; © XPhantom p64; **Siteright:** p204; **SMS Timber Frame Ltd:** p83; **Science Photo Library:** © Dr P. Marazzi/ Science Photo Library p23; **Steroplast Healthcare:** p7; **Superfoil.co.uk:** p95; **The NBS (NBS Create specification system):** p51; **Vulcascot Cable Protectors Limited:** p37.

Illustrations by Barking Dog Art.